GOD AND THE EVOLUTION OF ORGASM

Table of Contents

A World of Gratitude

to

The Hero Who Saved My Face.

As I started writing this book I was in a horrible medical accident in which my face was so badly burned I thought I'd be maimed for life.

I ran to my dermatologist, Dr Harold Lancer, "King of Cutis", who showed me a rare compassion and caring when trying to save my face from severe scarring. He saw me every day in a busy celebrity-laden schedule to tweak my treatment meticulously, insuring that I had the best chance to heal, when the doctor that caused the burn on my skin wouldn't even return my phone call or see me when I told him his treatment had gone seriously awry. It was Dr. Lancer's healer's heart as much as his unparalleled technical brilliance that got me through this crisis. Without that level of care I don't know how anyone can call him or herself a doctor. If only there were more doctors like him--and he has a pithy sense of humour to boot.

It's those that are there for you in your deepest moments of despair that you remember most gratefully!!!

Acknowledgments

Special Thanks to two friends who really went to bat giving me their time and brilliance to critique this work. They were always there to bounce ideas off of. Invaluable!!!

Marni Kamins

With your toddler and everything that comes with that, I was surprised that you took the time to give me one of the most thorough critiques and you read my book twice! When you ask for a favor such as this, you see just how intelligent your friends are. Your support was such a great gift! Yay to the sisterhood!!

Chris Ward

You always have said that you are everyone's best friend and now I know why. You lend an exacting professional eye and attitude to everything you do, even when it's gratis. Laughing with you throughout our creative sessions made the homestretch an experience I will always treasure. It's the fun that counts on this journey and Lord knows we have fun!!

Many thanks to these friends that were involved in supporting this project coming to fruition.

Don Greco

Alfonso García

Leon Henderson-MacLennan

Youm Kim

Gisela Kirby

Marty Kulman

Cody Lamarche

Gus Lira

Benjamin

Don Steele

Alan Steinfeld

Barry Krutchie – He hasn't done anything yet, but I'm thanking him in advance, because being the friend that he is when the book comes out he will most likely do something very special in support. Thanks babe!

Dedication

This book is dedicated to my parents Edna and James, who gifted me a rare trust as a child that instilled a confidence to go out and explore the world unhindered by fear or convention. They allowing me to seize the adventures of my wildest dreams, such as in the story told in this book.

With all the love and support we have always shown each other, they always have encouraged me to think for myself and be my own person. With the strong and varying personalities within our family, although we don't always agree, our support for and pride in each other is always unequivocal.

This unwavering support is exemplified in a story I love to tell about my parents' reaction to the title of my book. My father being the intellectual, agnostic, leaning toward atheism professor heard the title of this book and said: "You don't want to use the word GOD in the title. You don't want people to think you're not intelligent!"

Then my mother, on the other hand, who is very open-minded, but is much invested in a proper image says: "God is fine in the title, but couldn't you take ORGASM out of the title? What are people going to think? It's a little over-the top!"

Well, if I listen to both of them there would be no book!! We had a good laugh about it and they accepted the title was perfect since it was literally what the book was about

Even though the topic was not ideal for them they are still so proud!!!

My mom even edited my book, one orgasm at a time!

Love You!

My greatest wish is that my story inspire you to go on your own quest to discover the magic and majesty of your own soul.

Introduction

Have you ever had one of those magical moments you know you will never forget your entire life? A time so special that if you were to die at any moment you know you would be dying feeling full, content, for you have fulfilled your life's purpose?

I have! And this is my story.

When I look back on my life, all moments have led up to this time, intersecting at just the precise moment where circumstance has met destiny and a wondrous window of opportunity opened a new world–a sublime way of being! No prince, rock star or hero could have had it better, for these moments have been a time to shine and rise to a Godly state, savior of my own immortal life. Amidst the daily struggles that never cease, a dream of a lifetime came true for me!

I won the lottery of God's love.

This is the true story of a journey toward enlightenment of the kind that is oft never told, for all the lofty tales of awakening and spiritual quest leave out the normal, the material world, the physical, and the sexual. The lessons of awakening would be incomplete without the nuance of the mundane context in which spiritual ecstasy can appear and without the knowledge of how the most human of traits such as humor and laughter are our best companions in the exploration of the divine, as the mundane mingles with the magical at any given moment.

For there will not be a part of our being that will not be rocked and rearranged. Even the very nature of how we feel pleasure shall fan out in new directions yet unimagined. Something as earthly and carnal as an orgasm will be a vehicle to explore the cosmos of our being, the sacred connection to all that makes us ONE in God Self. For the otherworldly and fantastical to be real magic, it must in the end sow the seeds of practicality on this earth.

Everyone has a magic egg! That one place that holds the entire damn up, the soft spot, the way in. And, if we find a way to crack the magic egg, the lessons of the inner light open like a floodgate, realizing our divided self into our Whole self. The magic egg is a place in our being that is the entry point that lifts the veil to behold our inner wisdom.

A few weeks before my egg was cracked and my life was turned on its head, I had a dream that I know now was not just a premonition of things to come, but an initiation into the dialogue with God that was on the verge of igniting my soul with the fire bliss that the saints who have encountered divine visitations speak of.

I dreamt I was in an unkempt, old, nineteen-twenties-built bungalow in some gang-infested hood in Los Angeles. It had tasteless, worn, mismatched recycled furniture that smelled from too many years of old unwashed ass sitting on it and it appeared to be either someone's junk hauled off the curbside, sourced from the Goodwill, or perhaps stolen from some crackhead neighbor that just passed away. But despite the demoralizing appearance of this place, there was magic in the air!

The ugliness of the room was disconcerting and embodied despair and stagnation, but the air was palpable with the vibrant presence of the bright light of God! There was an extra glow of light that shed brightness and vibration in the room and gave a crisp clarity and rich color saturation to everything, permeating a sense of happiness throughout and lifting my spirit up and out of the dead-end life the room portrayed and giving a feel of hope and promise.

I took in the room in a second's time and then my eyes dropped to see a lioness in a cage just two feet in front of me, next to the bottom of a staircase in front of the door. She seemed to be a pet, calm and settled. There seemed to be no one home to give answers as to what this exotic animal was doing there. The front door was open and it was night. The streets seemed peaceful and abandoned. It was as if the world of people had vanished and it was just me and the lioness.

The moment I saw the lioness so majestic, fierce and strong, I suddenly became her, in her body, looking out through her eyes, through the cage. There wasn't a comforting familiarity to my surroundings, even though I felt I had been there for some time, waiting. I, as the lioness, did not like my surroundings. I just longed to go home and I knew what that should be, in the wild, in nature, where I could roam.

The light that made the room glow pacified me and kept my spirits healthy and high even if I was in the cage. Then, in an instant, I popped back into my human body and opened the cage. Then I popped back into being the lioness and walked out of the cage, out of the front door. It was my time to go back where I belonged, to the lush jungle teaming with life where I could be free!

I awoke with a feeling of meaningfulness that lingered, for the dream had been so real, it had already altered me somehow and permeated me with the knowing that something big in my life was about change: <u>A new freedom was on the rise!</u>

I was born with a drumbeat in my soul that has set the course of my life marching me towards freedom: The freedom to unleash all freedoms, each and every one. The voice toward freedom says: "anything to be more alive!"

I believe the innate desire toward freedom is instinctual in us all. It drives evolution itself; and part of the grand plan here in the cosmos is to evolve to our maximum potential. It is the flow of the creative force. Our survival depends on our freedom to evolve.

But what did that call to freedom mean personally to me? I felt I had been afforded by birth so many freedoms. I was white, born in America, the land founded on freedom, to an upper middle class, very open-minded, intellectual family that supported my dreams and talents, brought up in one of the most beautiful towns in the United States: Pacific Palisades, California.

Freedom means many different things to many people: The freedom of equal treatment in the eyes of the law and in society, equal opportunity, the freedom to worship as you please, the freedom to love whoever you please and how you wish, the freedom to follow your bliss vocationally, the freedom of speech and expression.

So what freedom did the drumbeat compel me towards when I seemed to have them all? I longed for a freedom I could only imagine and dream of, for it is rare indeed. I longed for a freedom that I didn't even know existed or what it really was until I experienced it. The freedom to truly know what lies in the soul, not figuratively as a test of my character or mettle in the world, not through a biased religious context or a manipulating intermediary, but pure, direct, and clean. My own essence as daughter of creation itself, the direct experience of my soul!

One can free the soul and still be shackled by the laws of convention. So freedoms shall come at different times in their own order to us. But the freedom of the soul in enough people will free the world in all ways someday.

And so my story of freedom and the most magical time of my life begins...

1

"A Date with Destiny"

Venice, California

I was driving to see a new masseur to work on my stiff neck, when a calm, like warm milk being poured on my head, descended, saturating my body with a feeling of stillness. Everything slowed down; details of life became more intense. I became fixated on the colors of the traffic light, first red and then green. I had slipped into a very present moment that always makes life come into a technicolor high-definition experience. The magician's cloak of changing perception was being shaken and the not very attractive route I was driving down Lincoln Boulevard was showing hints of the vibrant whimsical land of OZ.

I've been meditating since I was thirteen and have had mind-altering experiences descend during meditation and also in mundane moments, so I was not shocked or worried. This was a familiar event even if I hadn't experienced it in a while. I just observed it and hoped the openness that was granted to me through the calm would help me release the neck tightness and the underlying stress I had been locked into because of an imminent "break-up" that loomed in front of me. It was like being on death row. The mental struggle and fear of knowing a part of me was about to die was perhaps more torturing than the final death itself. I was so relieved to have this sense of ease start to reclaim itself in my body since the emotions of a dying five-year relationship had my heart and now my shoulder and neck in vice. What was worse, I had not been keeping a regular meditation practice, compounded by the fact that my boyfriend and I were partnering on a project I thought may go belly-up if we were no longer together. The tension caused by the flailing relationship was a Molotov cocktail for my emotions.

I pulled up to an apartment building that looked like a run-down high school in the projects: patchy lawn, peeling paint, no flowers, some trash blowing across the courtyard in front and between the buildings. The wind whistled and I thought I was looking at a snapshot of what the world would look like after a nuclear disaster: empty, barren, lifeless. Was it here where the masseur whom I had booked a month or more in advance lived? It had taken several phone calls to even get him to call me back! But he had come highly recommended by a top physical therapist, Annette. She herself has an amazing reputation and is flown around the world by wealthy clients when they are injured. I trusted that this would entail a quality massage, regardless of the external appearance of the location where it would take place.

I had asked Annette if she would do a series of bodywork sessions on me herself, because I felt my shoulders were rounding and my posture was being affected by my emotional turmoil. I am very familiar with bodywork since I was a professional ballet dancer and had serious bodywork my whole life. It had transformed my body before, but unbeknownst to me, this time it would transform my heart, my soul.

Instead of doing the bodywork herself, Annette enthusiastically suggested that I see someone she had just taken a new massage course from, Thaddeus Young, Thad for short. She said that she sensed I was ready for a heart opening. I was already well aware of that. I wanted to go back to wearing my heart on my sleeve, not around my neck as pain. Her words would prove to have a much deeper meaning than what I took them for at the time, now that I look back.

I saw a man waving to me from his apartment and figured it was Thad.

I entered the tight-fitting apartment living room painted a sterile, hospital-green color. The table was laid out in the center and even though the color of the walls was off putting, the place was cozy inside, like a cocoon within the unloved and abandoned exterior of the building.

Thad reminded me of the Cheshire cat from Alice In Wonderland. Not that he had a big fat face and was sticking his tongue out and rolling his eyes, but his giant, easy smile was of a mischievous, yet wholesome contentment that suggested "fun." Although his smile spoke volumes, the rest of him was non-assuming: a slender, tall man in his thirties, closely cropped dark hair that outlined the contours of his head, barefoot, dressed in comfortable, black, yoga pants and tank top. And just as he was comfortable in his clothes, he seemed to be living comfortably in his body, like favorite fuzzy slippers feel.

We sat on Thad's couch and drank a tea that I was told would be good for our session. I looked into his eyes and felt a deepening of the heightened state of being that I had been feeling on the drive. The late afternoon, magic-hour sun spread across his face lighting it warm and crisp, ideal for a picture. I wish I had had a camera to commemorate the day, as it would be the beginning of a new and unexpected journey. He didn't talk much or explain anything in particular or in depth. I shared with him my shoulder, neck, and relationship dilemma that needed "fixing" and told him I was a veteran of deep-tissue work. He seemed kind and gentle and I was ready to hop on that table to relieve the stress, so we got to it.

Music played, a New Age, tribal, yoga musical genre that seemed meant to stir emotions, not just to relax and sleep like the usual nondescript stuff played in massage sessions when masseurs are hoping you'll drift off to sleep so they don't have to work so hard. This was meant to evoke and provoke feeling and start an inner dance.

He asked if I was comfortable being topless and I said yes, although I felt a bit of resistance since it was our first time. We women guard our breasts and yet flaunt them like mana from heaven in America. They've been so sanctified, worshiped, and sexualized that they are no mere body part, but a gateway drug to sex. I coyly took of my bra and with that gesture of trust was a real willingness to be openhearted again. I tend to put on a bold front in life so he probably didn't notice my shyness.

Thad worked on my neck deep-tissue style and it hurt! I took deep, endless, slow breaths as I was taught by my other therapeutic body workers in order to release the tension and allow the massage to go deeper.

Then he lifted my arm and started to work in my armpits. Wow! What a bundle of painful nerves. No one had ever worked in my pits! He told me he wanted me to take a yogic release breath, a quick double exhale, every time the pain became very intense, instead of the deep, slow, relaxing breaths. In between the painful prodding he would do simple caresses across my lower abdomen and arms. He leaned in and would breathe with me after the pain and I would mirror his breathing.

The sex in my almost-over relationship had been gone for a while and my body was starving for touch. But beyond the simple touch aspect, my senses were responding in all kinds of ways from this therapy of breath, caress, and painful release that I had not experienced in a massage before. Thad put his head close to mine so that I would hear his low internal rumbling growl, a pleasurable, purposeful exhale growl of release. His body scent reminded me of an ex-lover's that smelled like pot and the color yellow, a memory that heightened my sensual awareness. I mimicked his internal growling to release the pain.

Suddenly, my body started to rumble from deep within like an almost inaudible voice in the distance. Then coming closer and louder, the rumbling started to shake my whole body. I was shivering and quivering uncontrollably no matter how I tried to stop it. Then it went up to my head and my jaw was chattering. I felt as if I was in an arctic freeze.

Thad asked me if I was all right. I stated the obvious: that I was cold and couldn't stop shaking for the life of me, but that I was OK. He kept working and moved to my hip and legs.

The shaking continued! I became increasingly uncomfortable and at what exact body part he was working on I don't remember, but one single tear came out of each eye with no particular emotion. I call these soul tears. They represent a release of energy that reconnects me to my soul, like a sigh from the lacrimals. Sometimes there are memories of emotions and feelings that are beyond human understanding that stream from the greater aware-ness of the soul.

Bam! The dam burst with those two tears and energy flooded, gushed, and rushed down my arms and hands. I was swimming in a sea of warmth that spread all over my body, and I was relieved of this odd shiver-ing tremble. I lay in delight, basking in awe at the power of the energy that flowed down my arms and hands. This was no ordinary trickle of tingling energy current. This was a waterfall of electricity that had manifested itself with the release of the soul tears.

Then after some time, say half an hour, the waterfall energy that rushed down my arms receded and I was swimming in sheer comfort in my body. Relaxed, warm, feeling the pulses of my body swelled open into a healthy sense of being alive and vigorous.

At the end of the session, we sat on his couch and we spoke a bit about my experience. It all seemed very normal to him, which should have been a tip to me that this was not just "a massage." He didn't explain any-thing out of the ordinary. Perhaps he thought Annette had spoken more in detail about what exactly his work was about. I was still under a spell of ignorance as to what was going to unfold with Thad's bodywork.

I had no specific idea as to what had happened, but I've been around enough meditations, healers, yogis, gurus and body workers to know this guy had something special and it was powerful. I instantly booked a double session, but to my disappointment I would have to wait two and a half months before he had an opening. But that wait turned out to be a valuable part of the process, because I was about to slowly unwind, unravel in prep-aration to become unhinged – in an intense and profound way!

I went home and totally forgot about my shoulders and neck. All I could muse about was what an interesting experience I had had and what more this work might evoke. This guy had something and it was tangible and would help jump start me back into spiritual exploration that was so dear to me.

* * *

"Hi Hungry" My boyfriend lovingly greeted me by one of my many nicknames with a heartfelt kiss that was getting rare these days. We'll call him Double Double with Cheese his self-proclaimed nickname at the time.

Once I asked him why he loved me so much and he said it was be-cause his whole life he had felt he had to be the man in control, cool, suave, but with me he could be his silly, goofy side. He could relax and be real and that made him feel comfortable and loved by just being himself. He said he could be a "Double Double with Cheese" as he patted the very small amount of girth he had gained that I suppose he felt conscious of around his midriff.

I hadn't even noticed it. He had taken on some of the physical perfectionist attitudes that come with living in Los Angeles.

Double Double was a dapper fellow who liked to dress in suits and carry himself with a touch of elegant arrogance. Quick and spry, he moved as one much younger than his age. He had fine boyish features and hair that could rule the world. His eyelashes were long enough to pet and the hair on his head was so strong that I think you could tie it to a train and he could pull the train along successfully, like they do in those "Strongest Man in the World" contests, without ripping his hair out. I tested the strength of his hair once with his consent. I pulled so hard, steadily, that I practically lifted him up from the chair, but he didn't even feel it, didn't hurt him at all and not one hair came out of his head. If you grew it out I think you could trim it into different creatures and it would hold its shape like a hedge. Needless to say, his hair was a wonder.

It was a beautiful compliment to me that I made him feel he could be a Double Double with Cheese, loved for who he was and not for some "James Bond' image he felt he had to live up to. I can't imagine living into one's forties and not feeling comfortable enough to be oneself instead of having the need to put on an act all the time. How could he have stood it all those years?

"How was your massage?" he asked as a lead into what he really wanted to know.

"Great. It was interesting. I had this flood of energy come down my arms…I felt a release," I explained.

"Good. So how is the rewrite on "Sexual Healing" coming along? We have a deadline here. Avenue wants to see it. Get it going." He lay down the facts of what he really wanted to speak about, which was not the massage.

"Sexual Healing" is the story of Bill Masters and Virginia Johnson, the first sex therapists in the world. I was chosen to write the script of their story for Avenue Pictures. I was flown to Saint Luis, Missouri to interview Virginia Johnson so as to capture her first-hand perspective of their famous story.

"I'm done. Left it on your desk," I replied proudly with some playful in-your-face attitude.

"Great! I'll read it tonight. Let's grab some food. I'm starving. Where do you want to go?" he announced, as he grabbed his coat. Double Double with Cheese never wanted me to cook. He always wanted to eat out or get take out. Not that my cooking was horrible. In fact, I don't think he ever let me cook one meal for him. He just liked to decide what he wanted to eat at the last minute. I think after a long day's work for both of us, he just wanted us to relax together.

The dying relationship and the tensions that surrounded it already seemed a little brighter after the session with Thad. Optimism was alighting from the fire of hope that had been rekindled in my heart. I went back to my daily routine, feeling that I had been pointed in the right direction to find my way out of the tension and back to the stress-free body and calm heart through which I liked to live life.

2

"The Quickening"

I must explain the drama that had led my heart to start distorting my shoulders as an expression of despair. I had recently become aware of the fact that my boyfriend was afraid of going to prison for tax evasion! Now you can understand why my life was sexless. Going to the "big house" will make anyone lose their appetite, shit in their pants, or lose their erection. He was not a criminal sort, but had a strange self-sabotaging rebellion in his mental frame. He seemed to think he was above having to deal with things such as taxes, waiting in line to renew a driver's license, and paying traffic tickets. He basically wouldn't pay tickets until there was a boot on his car or at least until they had tripled in price. He was a good, hard-working, very successful man, but could not see the logic of keeping this part of his life simple. He saw it as a burden he shouldn't have to deal with, which was so illogical, because the punishment for not dealing with these legalities was even more of a burden. Ah, figuring out the human psyche! He did pay his taxes when he worked for other people or if he had business partners that would file on his behalf, but if it was up to him, "forget about it."

Ironically, his father was an accountant! Some people eternally rebel even when it doesn't serve them anymore. I think he equated being responsible with living a boring, mundane life and he wanted to be James Bond-cool: women, money, and adventure flowing. He wanted more than the emotionally over-burdened existence his father's life portrayed and raged against it in an illogical and self-destructive way into his 40's. He was a lot of fun before the taxman caught up with him. He really knew how to make time spent together special, intense, and adventurous. But that was in the past.

Afraid that the patty wagon was going to come and drag his ass to Sing Sing he became a miserable, emotionally volatile, grumpy man. He had once been such a lively, humorous, playful, romantic, affectionate, and sexual partner. Now, he grunted at me without even looking at me for a greeting as he walked into the house and would go straight to his computer. He would no longer go out socially. He rarely wanted to have sex. He was the kind of guy who liked to be in control and take care of his woman. I think the whole experience of possibly going to jail or losing large amounts of his wealth to pay for his folly emasculated him. He didn't want me to see him fail so he was pushing me away.

After eight months of relating in this passive-aggressive and empty way I was a wreck. I was hoping he would realize that he wouldn't be going to prison, because the IRS prefers the money to punishment, unless you're a famous person they can make an example of; but he couldn't shake the fear. It had possession of him and he became an emotionally sick person.

I tried to be supportive and loving by just staying by his side while he went through it, but it seemed he wasn't budging from his fatalistic mood one bit. He was getting worse. I tried to make him laugh about it by telling him that I would visit him at the jail every day with a tuna sandwich, his favorite lunch food in the whole world, and he just got furious. Perhaps I wasn't in his shoes to know how he was feeling, but being with him started to feel punishing, almost emotionally abusive for me.

I sat down to eat dinner in front of the tube one night, soon after my bodywork with Thad, and I felt currents running up and down my legs. They weren't painful. I'd felt these tingling currents before in meditations. But as the weeks went by I started to feel them consistently. I wondered if there wasn't some nerve being pinched in my spine, but there was no pain association.

Then a sexual desire started to gnaw at me that I did not think to be unusual since I was in a sexless relationship. But it kept getting stronger, mushrooming into a distorted distraction. I would masturbate to climax and not feel like a drop of desire had been released. I wasn't eating anything different or taking aphrodisiacs like horny goat's weed. I wasn't around any man whose flirtations where making the juices flow or stimulating fantasy. I'd lay awake after pleasuring myself for the third time--not satisfied--and just assumed it had to do with the sexual frustration in the relationship.

Interestingly, it never occurred to me to cheat in the relationship. That was not an option for many reasons. I didn't want to lie to my partner. Also, this sexual energy didn't focus on an outward outlet of a man, anyway. It didn't make me feel like running out and fucking everybody or anybody for that matter. Maybe I would have felt different about this if I hadn't been in a relationship, but the energy was so strong I think I would've been scared to bring an unknown person into these new insatiable, uncontrollable energies that were new and disconcerting to me.

With the energy building, there came a voice that kept repeating: "It wants to go up...it wants to go up." I knew "it" meant the sexual energy. The currents in my legs and spine continued to widen as well. I basically stopped masturbating, because it didn't seem to be satisfying me in any way. It seemed to me that I had no way of directing this energy up or anyplace. It just kept building.

As the weeks went by I knew this was not normal, at least not for me. One day I was at my wit's end with this energy distracting me so intensely I couldn't even sit to write for more than ten minutes. I can usually sit calmly for hours at a time. This was crazy! I had a sexual pulsing in my whole body. My heart pulsed with sexual energy. Parts of my body I never knew could feel sexual, like my elbows were pulsating. In desperation I called a couple of friends that were veterans of meditation practice to try and get pointers on how to deal with this energy. They were not at home and I was feeling lost and overwhelmed by a sexual entity that had co-opted my body.

One morning when I couldn't sit and write I decided to start meditating to channel the energy and the sexual energy took the driver's seat. My legs uncrossed themselves from the normal Indian style meditation position I sat, legs bent toward my chest and spread, and a low moan split my being as it grew loud. My head bent back until it touched the ground behind me as if I was about to give birth. I cannot do this pose under normal circumstances. The pulsing moan from my heart and belly emanated out to mingle with life and I felt I was having sex with the universe, the ether, and I couldn't contain this force as I reached out to call it, to meet it, to merge with it, to expose my most powerful and raw heart. A heart-pulsating being, that I wasn't even aware was inside me, was emerging.

"Oh Lord, this is everything!" I screamed in my head. When I screamed "Oh God," it was literally God that I could attribute this orgasm to that would not let me out of its grip. It would not let me down. To be clear, it was not a vaginal contracting orgasm I was experiencing; it was my whole body contorting and moaning as an expression of orgasm. It was much stronger than a regular orgasm. It was transporting me into and informing me of another level of sexual experience.

Shaking, I eventually decided I needed to go do something else so as not to be caught in this act of as yet unexplainable "nasty," holy, and sacred initiation. When I say nasty, it is only because it felt like it was the type of pleasure we've always been taught we should hide. Can you imagine being caught making love to what appeared to be nothing, a ghost, the Holy Ghost of course, hopefully, the Ether. I had already had some interesting experiences and this was turning out to be the strangest for me, so I could imagine just how strange it would be for someone else to walk in on me moaning in these sexual/spiritual episodes. This specific, most intense meditation came on the day before my next "body working appointment" with Thad. It seemed perfectly planned. My time was up. Time for me to wake up!

The physical security I knew in my relationship and the lifestyle that was afforded by that relationship was destructing and I had been feeling lost emotionally. Now, I was lost in a new terrain of insatiable sexual desire and unexplainable spontaneous sexual experiences that were definitely not provoked by some mortal, manly musk phenomenon, but seemed to be the ether itself that titillated me and energized me. It was as if atoms were exploding inside of me, releasing a power I was not accustomed or fully comfortable with, even though it delighted and invigorated me.

Life was dissolving and rearranging itself and I was in full swing of the chaos that comes with such a transformation. And it came with more bells and whistles than I had bargained for, because there was a bridge into the unknown that was emerging, into the world of the primordial self, into the mystery of God, existence, and who I was. And with all the signs that this "force" displayed, expressing itself in a sexual manner I had not bargained for, I never thought once of not proceeding. There was no question that I would go down this road, come what may, and with the thunderbolt of the Gods, it would shock my body to new understanding of God, sex, and the meaning of life.

Since I was thirteen years old, I remember desiring and dreaming of the "Big E" (enlightenment), not much thought to the big "O" (orgasm). I guess I took the "mortal orgasm" for granted. What a surprise I had to find out that a stage of enlightenment would come through the purest essence of sex itself.

"Hey Thirsty!" Double Double with Cheese called out one of my other nicknames, which often had to do with my love for nourishment, as he came home just as I had brushed myself off and collected myself from having sex with the ether, the universe. This is one lover you can't hide in a closet. The Universe is one lover no one would ever expect or accuse you of cheating with.

"Avenue loves the script! They're thrilled," he announced. "Cary says that the script will take Avenue Pictures to the Oscars again!"

"I know. I was at the meeting with you a few weeks ago and he said the same thing then," I reminded him.

"Yeah. But you don't know we already have some mega A list actors interested," he burst out almost as if in song. "He thinks my baby's script may win an Oscar. Remember the first script that the first writer wrote and it was thrown out? That was a bloodless piece of shit! Well, this was your chance, you stepped in, and you made it happen. "Sexual Healing" is a winner, thanks to my baby!"

Sexual Healing was in the air in more ways than one...

3

"God Orgasm, Tea, & Lamb Chops"

I didn't feel comfortable divulging my sexual angst to Thad on our second appointment, so I kept mum. We drank his ritual tea and stared at each other in the hazy, particle-filled sunlight that streamed on his couch. It was at this point I started to feel the sloshing of the large meal of lamb chops and twenty vitamins that I had eaten in a hurry and wished I hadn't tried to shovel so many nutrients into my stomach before a bodywork session.

By the way, the tea was no "strange brew" of some mind-altering substance, unless you consider something akin to your Starbucks coffee a portal to a psychedelic experience and God awareness. We would have had a Utopian society on earth by now if that were the case. Thad serves either *yerba ma*te or *guaraná tea*, stimulants that contain some caffeine. (I can see the sales go up after the reading of the following account.)

Thad went into the other room, as he always does, to allow me to disrobe partially and slip under the sheets. I didn't have any extraordinary expectations or any expectation at all. Oftentimes when I've visited healers, their effectiveness is inconsistent. There is definitely a variable to just how powerful a healer is on a given day and how receptive a patient is. And perhaps, in the layers of life that we still do not understand fully, there are other reasons for these variables, maybe one of the endless types of karma that I've heard of. I don't necessarily believe in karma or profess to know how it would work, especially if there are so many kinds: personal, family, country, etc. But let's just say there was good karma due me and apparently it was about to club me in the head.

Thad began working on my neck, deeply and painfully, although I no longer was so focused on that issue, given the wave of sexual distraction that I was riding of late. Nothing strange happened. Then he worked down my arms. Everything still seemed normal. Even the icky pushing of a lamb chop and a vitamin stew that was not digesting, threatened to mutiny and jump ship. The rhythm of the music stimulated and loosened my body simultaneously. We did the yogic double-breath release.

Thad paused.

Then, with one finger he reached down and pressed my lower abdomen. Bam!! A sensation of energy, liquid fire, shot up my spine and burst from inside every cell of my body. I yelled with the force of unbridled ecstasy and surprise. The heat broke out into a full-body sweat, and in that instant I was a dripping, melting mess. It was hotter than a sauna, and it was more than good. It was bliss! The heat spontaneously moved me up onto my knees without even thinking. My mind was not in the driver's seat anymore. It just watched in utter disbelief. As my body slowly undulated and delicately gyrated, I was moved by this force to touch the most sacred thing I've ever felt – MY BODY!! As if I was both lover and beloved, giver and receiver, both the touch and the hand were receiving equal pleasure. I was one with this fiery force –THE LIFE FORCE ENERGY–too beautiful to almost contain. Yes. The body is the temple of the soul as it says in the Bible (Corinthians 6:19-20). Is this what Jesus meant? Is Heaven in every cell as the bliss of the creative Life Force Energy awareness in our bodies? I was entering my most sacred temple for the first time.

I was exploding over and over again in a unique flavor of pleasure that was both sexual and sacred at the same time. Sex and the sacred mingled in a way that was seamless: the innocence of pure ecstasy. I felt as though I may combust completely. "IT" was alive! A part of me was alive that I never knew existed! And yet I felt an understanding that "IT" was there all along. "IT" was there before time. "IT" knew about me when I apparently did not have full awareness of "IT." It was the overlord. I was a sub-particle of its awareness. "IT" is the real me not the "me" I "think" I am.

I moved up and down slowly on my knees reaching my hands out, just feeling the bliss course and pulsate through my body and release from some new dimension inside every cell. And it was talking to me. Not in words, but in an instantaneous knowing through what I would describe as the highest aspect of intuition.

It was informing me of a vastly superior wisdom to the intellect. My mind was humbled for it had thought it was the smartest aspect of my being since that is what we are taught in the Western world. The mind watched in awe and humbly deferred to this intuition, pouring out of every cell of the body. No wonder I had gotten so much wrong at different points in my life. I was looking to the wrong aspect of self for the answers. I had forgotten how to listen to God wisdom speaking through the intuitive body/heart intuition.

The signs are always there as a gross physical manifestation. How many times had my body/brain spoken to me on a cellular level, turning my stomach when I bought into a false belief system, making my hands cold or my core uneasy, hollow, when around people of masking subversive intentions? So many times I did not listen because I had lost the connection to my body/brain on how to clearly interpret what exactly these signs were telling me.

It was informing me about where to find not just happiness but bliss!! "The kingdom of God is within" every cell of your body. It is the fabric of absolutely everything! And we miss this in lieu of what? In lieu of fabrications of the intellect/mind.

In an instant I could see this was what everyone toiled for and ran around in circuitous ways seeking. And I realized that we must learn to connect to this direct source of bliss if we are ever to be fully satisfied: fully loved, fully alive, fully thriving, and achieving our potential as human beings!

So many instances of this life shot through my head, of human beings seeking this contact with bliss in ways that would only spark a faint memory of the fiery bliss that is this conscious force. Those who take drugs to feel love over pain, those who seek fame for love and approval, those who seek success and wealth to feel powerful and effective, and those who never can be satisfied sexually, are truly seeking the very essence of bliss of their own soul! If they only knew the direct line requires no outward object, gain, or pursuit. Unconditional love and acceptance are in the heart of every cell of the body temple!

Thad disappeared. He was never an object of sexual desire or lust, but here I was with his touch to my belly having an orgasm in every cell of my body. Yes, an orgasm, for this force is the ultimate sexual satisfaction I've ever had; equivalent to a million orgasms all at once. I was not in the cramped green apartment. I was in a red and orange world of swirling fire.

The Bible talks of the Original Sin, and as far as the energy was informing me, the Original Sin was forgetting about the Original Bliss! And forgetting the bliss leads us astray to do the wackiest and sometimes destructive things in order to recreate a pleasure that we instinctively crave: The Original Bliss that is The Life Force Energy – God! I didn't realize how lost I was until I felt this sense of happiness permeating my body. I finally felt like I was HOME! I didn't know I was living a life not fully at home in my body until that day.

Waves of soothing comfort, love, acceptance, and reverence for my body's capacity to be the answer, imprinted a new truth in my mind. I made sounds that must have made the neighbors worry about just what kind of chandelier-swinging sex we were having as Thad tried to cast out the demon-monkey from my soul. If you can imagine those sounds! I'm surprised they didn't call the police. Having sex with your own God-force energy can be very boisterous and obnoxious for the neighbors.

I was on my knees with my elbows by my side, forearms stretched out, palms up, and my head all the way back. I was in this one position that looked like an Egyptian hieroglyph for an hour. I have long hair down to my waist, and the pleasure heat extracted a sweat that dripped continuously from the ends. I never thought I could sweat so much. Pinned in this one position, I was in communion with a part of myself that was so new that it may be considered another entity that had descended upon me, but no, it was me. It is a larger, more complete part of me that oversees this smaller identity and was making itself clear and present.

Why had the wiser, most sacred and blissful part of me kept itself hidden, or perhaps I should say had only spoken to me in whispers my whole life, up until that day? Any self-consciousness left melted in sobs of gratitude for having experienced what made me feel completely undone as I felt such vulnerable pleasure. Why was it that I felt so vulnerable at this depth of my being? It was just the heart's deepest pleasure. Why did I feel I had to hide it from others?

I have experienced altered states, heightened states of awareness before, but this was different. My Larger Self had taken over and my mind had no say. I, the small me, was out of control in the powerful hands of the God-self me. "I" was not meditating. I was not trying to meditate. The Life Force Energy was meditating me!

Finally, Thad directed me to lie down, because he had to end this session. Bummer! I could have gone on lost in communion, but I managed to obey and lay down on the table. He covered my sweat-drenched body with a sheet and did some cranial work to ease me out of the session. I drifted off to sleep for a few seconds as Thad meditated and sang along with the music for a short while. He said it was time for me to go as he left the room for me to dress.

I opened my eyes and my mind was very quiet, spent, as if a part of it had been erased and I had a clean slate. I rolled off the table and used the sheet to towel dry my wetness. I felt a little shaky as I put my sweats back on. The sexual angst was gone. It had been released into my body, bathing, and coating my cells with a new sheen from which to see the world. My sexual energy build-up had launched me into a new dimension where I was open to a new clearer dialogue with God. The Life Force Energy was about to start communicating with me through everything.

Here I had tried to transcend the body, the senses, to contact God, my higher self. Perhaps I had misunderstood what the teachers and scriptures had said, for this higher self was in my body as sexual life-force consciousness that made me feel Heaven through my "pure" re-sensitized self. It was the sexual energy buildup that pushed me to deeper places in my soul than I had ever reached.

Thad came out. I really didn't have much I wanted to say as I basked in the awakened energy. But part of the session is to discuss the experience on the table, so I tried to express that I had just gone through the most intense experience of my life. I don't remember what I said.

I left the apartment and as I drove home, I had to call Annette. She didn't answer, so I left a message. "What the hell was that? What just happened?"

I was delightfully perplexed. These questions were not of great concern or worry. My mind could not hold onto such things as worry as it was so blown away into peace. I wondered if this was really what she meant when she said "I was ready for a heart opening." Why had she not told me? Is this what Thad does for everyone, or was this some special occurrence?

One thing I did know for sure was that what I had experienced was exactly what I had read about and heard gurus and swamis speak about in the Indian practice of yoga: "maha kundalini awakening." This great Life Force Energy is depicted as a serpent coiled at the base of the spine that when released, it purifies the chakras, the energy systems, and it opens the spiritual awareness. There is a lot of heat associated with the experience. I had a hunch that my fiery snake had been trying to release up my spine just as the voice in my head kept telling me when I was locked into unrelenting sexual angst, "IT" wants to go up."

Going against conventional teachings--for I had always been told that to invite a great connection to Spirit and open the kundalini it was best to not eat meat and to meditate on an empty stomach--my most earth-shattering awakening would happen on a full stomach of lamb and icky vitamins! The moment the kundalini shot up my spine, the sense of fullness from the lamb was gone. It was as if the energy evaporated it in an instant. It almost seemed like this opening was destined to happen no matter what circumstance was at play.

As a teenager, when I was about sixteen, I literally had dreamt about the exact experience: a liquid fire of bliss that made me identify myself as this pure sexual bliss energy and forget myself as an individual identity. In the end, it was not about following exact, niggling rules, but I think it had been a general lifestyle of health and meditation that prepared me for the awakening. It was not up to my "mind," but the power and wisdom of the Life Force Energy. When the kundalini energy is awakened, it thrashes its mighty tail at you and will knock you down no matter where you stand--lamb chops or no lamb chops.

When I got home I craved to be in nature. I had to feel the sun and the air so close, as if my life depended on it. I went hiking in the hills across from my home. In the air and the sun, I could feel the magic life-force energy. I was cocooned in this knowing, comforting me and keeping me awake to the power and magic all around. I felt my heart energy was so huge and my emotional static slate wiped so clean, that with every step I took, I was blessing the earth. I felt the sacred communion with the earth beneath my feet.

Just the last few months I had walked the same hiking path, but how different my relationship was then to my surroundings. Then I was praying and asking for blessings, relief from my emotional and physical pain, whereas now I was so full, I had nothing to ask for, but so overflowed with heart, that blessings flowed naturally out of me and into the world. This path that I had walked so many times was a mirror for my inner state. The dry, golden, tall grass swayed with the breeze at sunset and every cell in my body was pregnant with life.

Now, I understand the walking meditation done in the stone labyrinths. When you walk the same path over and over again, you will see how the beauty or blandness of that path changes in accordance to your inner state.

Feeling more into what it is to be alive and more aware of the precious, arresting beauty of everything, I was swathed in the understanding of the sacred relationship that was healing me, reconnecting me in so many ways. I had become detached in small ways that I was not aware of until this day of reconnection. I was reestablished in a timeless, Larger Self. I was feeling the world as myself. I was seeing the world through the eyes of my heart. Maybe this is what we are all searching for: How to let the heart of the "Larger Self" lead. Reconnection!

I could feel the wind at the top of the mountain as a Spirit, a consciousness. I could feel the flutter of the wings of a butterfly give me a precious chill of joy. My senses were juicy and raw like a newborn's. I had been reintroduced to my original openness and sensitivity. How important it is to protect this sensitivity to receive the layers of pleasure from the natural world and from the heart itself. I had become numb and I have always been considered a pretty centered, stable, and happy person. I could see that maybe the reason why so many people are running around crazed is because they have become numb, desensitized, perhaps over stimulated by things that have distracted them from the direct source energy. It had happened to me and I have had a meditation practice, I don't do drugs, I come from a stable and loving home, and never had what the world would consider a major trauma. However, the little events that were hurtful, confusing, distorted subtleties or societal programming in my life were filed away in my subconscious, building walls, running the show and keeping me from living fully. What else had been kept from me about my own fuller sense of self for reasons that were subconscious?

The natural world should feed us the pleasure that so many taste only artificially and thus end up harming themselves. The mind clings to strange distorted habits, seeking the security that can only be established through direct experience of the awakening and awareness of the Life Force Energy. It can be so simple to be satisfied when you sink into the layers of the heart of the Larger Self. The pleasure, the love we seek, exists. You may be satiated someday, too, if you are blessed by the awakening of the serpent.

With my new ability to feel beauty came a feeling that I had stepped out of a dulling membrane and I was seeing and feeling at a deeper level, but I was also much more vulnerable without the membrane. I realized I didn't want to be around people I didn't trust or that may not understand what I was going through. This was a sacred understanding of life that was growing in me and I wanted to cultivate it, protect it, so as not to lose the new sensitivity that had me in ecstasy.

I meditated in the garden that night and decided that I would stop my work and social life and make a mini-ashram, a sanctuary in my home to give myself the time and space to look into what this new emerging Life Force was showing me. Luckily, my home and garden face the mountains, so the natural surroundings fed the experience even more.

Oh, there was the boyfriend issue! The influence of living with a boyfriend that was so negative at the time could have been detrimental to my vulnerable, sensitive state. But since he was so wrapped up in his crisis, instead of feeling lonely, his distance was a relief and an opportunity to allow me to recede into a world of my own: A mystic world of intense new energy that I wanted to venture into and that, apparently, I had no say in the matter. "IT" was growing through me and around me, devouring the world I knew and unfolding a reality of initiation and understanding of the deeper realms of the mind, the wisdom of higher, whole-self, and the sexual power of the Life Force Energy – God.

It was as if I was realizing I was a different breed altogether. Perhaps I had not been taught about what the potential of a human being is. Something had been left out before, but now I felt I was the most blessed person on earth, enlightened to the endless beauty in my heart and in the world. This is all I had wanted my whole life and it was happening.

In this life-changing moment I saw my story unfolding with an odd set of circumstances which made me wonder if there was a destiny beyond my conscious understanding or was it just the strangest of coincidences. Here I was writing a screenplay called "Sexual Healing," the story of the first sex therapists in the world and I was having a sexual healing myself! A sexual healing of the spiritual kind. But *this* was not in *their* books!

4

"The Holy Gauntlet"

The events of the day and my new relationship with the "Life Force Energy" so overshadowed everything that I don't remember much of my relating with my boyfriend that night. I told him what happened and that I would be retreating from my normal activities and work project to conserve this "happening." He was always supportive of my spiritual practice so he was on board. My family was notified and on-board. They all needed to know that going into my shell was a calculated, positive behavior and that I was not going boldfaced crazy.

None of my family is into the type of spiritual practice or have had the mind-altering experiences that I've had, but they always were respectful of my path and thought it was very positive for me. I was stepping into the unknown and anything could happen. Based on what had been happening, I didn't want them to think I was going insane if some new kundalini expressions started to happen. This was out of the framework of what we all knew as normal.

I nestled into the darkness of my bed and for the first time in a long time I felt totally at ease, totally contented, comforted, cocooned from all worries. My nerves felt soft, coated by a light of protection.

I slept long and hard and when I got up, my boyfriend was gone and I was alone in the house. I did my morning meditation in the yard. The kundalini energy tingled to life in my body until I did not feel my body at all, just the energy.

And so that began a journey of navigating new otherworldly experiences, ecstasies, subconscious pain being unearthed as it became conscious. My new life was like stepping into an enchanted forest full of the most unbelievable delights of the heart and a gauntlet of trials that tested the very strength of my soul and sanity.

Early one evening I was writing an account of my experience that had stimulated the newly freed kundalini to swirl through and about me. The act of recounting the experience caused me to relive the experience. The "energy" was pleased that I would remember and recount it in any form, through writing or speaking and it was gifting me with its presence. I sat crying and sweating. The heat! The heat! What was up with the heat? And I felt bliss and gratitude. I liked everything about the experience, but the heat can be uncomfortable at times.

Then, later that evening, I excitedly shared with my mother the groundbreaking and mystifying events of the day and again the "energy" leaked out of my heart in reverence and out of my pores in sweat. I felt a little frail in my vulnerability and a little weak from all the sweating, but it was worth the amount of satiating feelings I was encountering. Something as simple as breathing was intoxicating. Breathing gave me the sensation of an inner massage. Again, speaking my truth made the "energy" pleased and it swirled and whirled in me as the most tender love.

The next morning after meditation I walked to the kitchen thinking I wasn't really hungry. Suddenly, in a split second I became so famished, I felt I was going to vomit. I hurriedly made some oatmeal, but after only two bites my pipes shut. I was stuffed. My solar plexus felt very strange. I felt very light, see-through, as if there was not much physical matter to me.

I went with whatever presented itself and didn't worry. I knew things would be happening that were different. I spent a lot of time meditating and got some books that Thad recommended I read over the next few days.

At night I would meditate outside and a new love for the darkness of night came to me. I would do the yoga breath (two quick exhales) and the kundalini would unleash and meditate me, effortlessly lost in the sheer bliss of breath and the new companionship of this Larger Self that was showing me my heart was the doorway to Eden on Earth again. We have all the raw materials and makings for Eden. The only thing missing is the deepest memory of the heart. The heart is the wormhole that connects us to all others and to our universal self. If you go deep enough you will find yourself in the heart of others and of all things.

The next day I went out to meditate and my solar plexus felt a sudden pain and I felt like I would vomit again. I decided I was going to stay in meditation and I asked for understanding. It reminded me of a pain I used to feel when I was nine and I had ulcer symptoms that would keep me from school.

The ulcer pain in my childhood occurred at a time that in my striving for attention and love from my world, I became a perfectionist. And in the world of ballet where I was emerging as a star, everyone was on a diet, so I became borderline anorexic. I say borderline, because I didn't want to hurt myself, I wasn't terrified of being fat, nor did I see myself as fat. There was just the mentality that I was willing to do anything to ensure that I pleased those around me: teacher, parents, friends, all seemed extraordinarily pleased that I was prima ballerina-star material. If I had been in another sport that said I should be heavier, I would've made an effort to gain weight.

Again, day after day the kundalini was talking to me through my body. I felt the fragility of being shaken into having access to a whole new world where the archives of my life were so secretively kept – in my subconscious. I kept fighting with my bizarre appetite throughout the day that was like a strange fever. In a second I would be thrown into a desperate starvation and the next minute, when I would sit to eat, I would lose my appetite. What was my stomach trying to tell me? What memories were held in these physical manifestations of pain? I followed my stomach down the path of thoughts and feelings from the past. It was like opening up to a specific chapter in my life. And each expression of pain has a story. I felt I was barely singed, not burned, from this early period of my life, so I was surprised that it came up. The story I told myself was that of someone who came away unscathed, but apparently there was something that I needed to heal and come to terms with from that time.

During the period of my childhood that I described, my parents got worried and confronted me about dieting and I thought they were nuts. First, they wanted me to be the best and then they were bugging me about doing what I had to do to be the best. I also didn't believe my mother's warning that dieting could harm the body. After all, why was it that everyone I knew in my world of ballet, that was also thin, dieted if it was harmful? Anyhow, one day my mother was reading to me passages from a couple of books on Anorexia called "The Golden Cage," and "The Best Little Girl in the World" about how those that suffer anorexia and diet to an extreme end up damaging their health. She started to list the signs of diet damage. One of them was excessively dry skin…

Wait! She was making it up, I thought, because at that moment I was getting out of the bath and I noticed that my skin was unusually dry and flaking. I accused her of lying. She showed me the quote in the book. I was floored. I realized she was being truthful in saying that I was hurting my body, so I stopped dieting that day.

I never wanted to hurt myself with the dieting. I just didn't believe my parents that I was doing something wrong. I had lost faith in what authority was saying, because it seemed like they were giving me contradictory messages all the time. I thought I finally discovered how to be successful in their eyes and what made them happy and now they were telling me not to be "the best." That damn ballet is an art for the unhealthy. There hasn't been a J.Lo or Beyoncé booty in the ballet world to break the unhealthy perception of the ideal ballet body, yet.

The moment I realized the truth, I changed. The physical habit of eating normally was easy to alter, but by that time, the mental habit and the chemical changes from not eating left me a little emotionally volatile for a while. There was a hardness and resistance that was unusual for a nine-year-old that probably came from the discipline that I had enforced on myself in ballet and from starving myself. Starving oneself does take unusual discipline. Perhaps I lost a bit of trust in what the world was telling me. And how do you protect yourself from that? How do you know who to trust after that? And again, I was seeking love and approval and yet, my family was so loving to me!

I remember my mother dragging me to a therapist and I absolutely hated the idea of going to a psychologist. I refused and stopped walking. She just kept walking and little by little, I followed. But after the first session, I loved it! I realized aspects of my inner self mattered and could be expressed. I realized being an emotional being would not get in the way of me being "productive." It wasn't a waste of time to have, share, and express feelings--as my father unfortunately believed and conveyed to me.

My mother said that my anorexic flare-up affected their relationship. The problem that manifested itself in me she was experiencing in her marriage. My father would never make time for her emotional needs and ignored her when she wanted to communicate. There was always a book to write, an interview, a class, a social event that needed focus and no distraction such as "weak emotion" could get in the way.

My mother thanked me for being the sensitive one that brought this family issue to light. She made me feel special for being the one to herald a healthier truth even though it was scary and painful for the family. I guess I was the sacrificial lamb–that got to be resurrected.

My father went to therapy and learned how important it was to take the time to communicate with me. I was always much closer to my mother and a little afraid of my father. He was so cold, not to be confused with not being fun. He was a lot of fun! He just loomed like a dark figure that didn't accept a part of who I was, the emotional side, and that is a big part of any human being, especially a woman. There was an ominous feeling of an impenetrable wall. But through this experience, he took endless time to sit with me when I was emotional and we became best of friends.

I went to a therapist for only four months, after which he terminated my therapy saying I didn't need him. He told my parents that he did not worry about me because he thought that I was very resourceful. I liked the therapy so much that I wanted to continue and was saddened that he insisted that I let him go.

My mother said that he was very impressed by my dream life. I could dream something and if I so desired, I would pick-up wherever I left off in the dream the next day. It was perhaps a premonition of abilities that would come to me later in the dream world.

I changed my physical habits and my mental obsessive-thought loops of food and perfection broke away in pieces to a new way of thinking soon after. I prayed a lot for the food thoughts to go away completely. Fortunately, I was young enough and in the grip of the bad habit for such a short time, that those thoughts did disappear – completely! Many who enter in this food-thought loop addiction have more trouble re-patterning because they are caught up in it for a longer period of time and I understand it has a stronger hold on the psyche the older a person is.

Now as an adult and after my kundalini awakening, my solar plexus was bringing me back to that time of pain. My soul, through my solar plexus had once told me that I was not on the right thought path. And here it was again. Perhaps there was some reminiscence, some subtle misguided imprint from that time still at work in my subconscious wanting to be seen, wanting to be released so that I could replace it with a new insight, a clearer, deeper, more self-serving truth to run my life by. Anything that blocked my connection to this higher self, had to be purged, and my body was letting me know where the subtle blocks were held.

Then one blindingly sunny day by the bougainvillea in my garden I meditated. I internally swung between bliss and the most intense nausea. I decided to hold my ground and continue to meditate come what may, vomit or not. Then an image of a very famous Indian Saint Nityananda came to me and he put his large hand on my stomach. The nausea instantly went away and I had a long, deep, blissful immersion into the joy energy. This nausea and hunger pendulum stopped that day, but the spiritual gauntlet continued to unravel blocks.

I now tried to avoid my boyfriend in more ways, beyond responding to his trying to block me out. Cohabitating and sharing all the earthly matters at that time made it impossible not to have a lot of contact with him and it was a matter of time before there would be some interaction that would challenge my "home ashram." After all, I've never been in an actual ashram where there were no personality conflicts. So, what was I thinking? How could I possibly assume I could put the messiness of life aside just because I was having orgasmic conversations with God?

I was dressing in my bedroom when my boyfriend descended on me with an emotional avalanche of anger and frustration. The memory of the resolution of this event is so profound that it overshadowed whatever the trite complaints were about, for I have no recollection as to what he wanted to fight about.

I felt a fight for justice build in me and I tried to explain my different opinions in the matter at hand. He wasn't listening and kept raising his voice in frustration without letting up. I felt myself about to engage in battle to set him straight, when the "energy" picked up around me and swirled inside me like a tornado, pulling my attention away from what was going on outside. I closed my eyes.

The swirling energy was so strong it made me feel a little disoriented from the outside world, while still being steady in my interior world. I felt like I was shot down a tunnel to my core. The kundalini energy spoke:

"You cannot waste your energy in this petty argument. It means nothing. You need to be wise on how you expend your energy from now on. This new force is a gift and is needed to journey to the higher states. Do you want to waste your energy fighting with someone who can't even listen in this moment or do you want to be here with me? You need your energy to unveil the pearls of wisdom of the soul, and now that you know how sacred and precious this energy is, you also know it is irresponsible to waste it. Be aware of how you direct your energy. It's up to you."

Even though the question was put to me from my Higher Self, it felt as if the energy was so strong, I truly didn't have a choice. My Higher Self, the awakened Life Force Energy was calling the shots.

I explained to my boyfriend exactly what was happening. I told him that I just couldn't engage in a battle in this altered, vulnerable state I was experiencing. He totally shut up! On the spot, he dropped it and walked away. I don't know if it was the way that I said it or perhaps he could see that I was seriously having an unusual experience, but he didn't seem mad or upset.

I realized that the issue never really mattered to him. He needed to fight with someone to release energy himself and he had been drawing me into a nitpicking argument using me as a scapegoat for his misfortunes.

I was so glad I protected my energy. And I was even more amazed at the clear and feeling dialogue I was having with the "Life Fore Energy." The *maha* kundalini was showing me how to use this new energy for traveling into the heart. There was a new greater Spirit guiding me. It was, magically, my own higher self.

That night, while sleeping, my mind/awareness showed me the dimensions I worked on simultaneously without usually knowing. I became conscious that I was, while still deep in slumber, experiencing the phenomenon known as lucid dreaming. Many people have had this experience. At the same time that I was dreaming, my mind was having a dialogue with itself about something completely different than what was happening in the dream. I was discussing how and when to break up with my boyfriend and how that would change my life.

Adding on to the experience, I started to want to influence my dream consciously. I was dreaming that I was going down the street and I decided I was going to peer into the houses to see what was going on in the private life of others; a voyeuristic thrill drove me. And, at the same time, I was consciously manipulating the events in my dream, and having discussions of my relationship demise. I was marveling that I was doing all these things at once!!!

It's as if I always played so close to my dollhouse that I could only be aware of one room at a time, but then I took a few steps back and I had an overview of the many rooms in the house at one glance. I could see that my mind worked on different levels at once, whether I was aware of it at all times or not.

Another night, totally out cold in slumber, an energy bolt shot up my spine and literally stood me up on the bed. I was waking up as I flew up onto my feet to find myself standing on the bed like a cat landing with firm balance. The energy we have hidden in our body can be more than a mystery to us all.

Something new was happening. I could read people in a whole new way. It was so easy to see what insecurities their mannerisms expressed. It could be a simple gesture. This is not to say I would have detailed knowledge of a person's past or why they were the way they were. I wasn't psychic. I would just be able to see the sadness through a smile, the insecurity in a very socially adept individual. I could read the subtleties of body language more clearly. I guess it takes one to know one and since I was observing how sadness or insecurity where held somatically in me, I was able to see it in others.

I observed what appeared to be an epidemic in our society that astounded me. Most people are sexually unsatisfied! They can be having an extremely active sex life and yet they are not satisfied. They may be attractive, in shape, sexy people having a lot of sex, but their mannerisms revealed that they were not at home in their body. They were unsettled, disconnected with the pleasure that is in their body on a cellular level.

Could it be that without the direct connection to the Life Force Energy in the whole body we will always be unsettled? Do we need to feel the God Orgasm in each cell to be satisfied?

After a few weeks of seclusion, I ventured back into my regular work routine and contact with friends. I felt like staying in my little "ashram home," but I was not ready to abandon my work. Moving back into the routine didn't slow down the epiphanies. I vowed to protect my budding sensitivity that allowed me to see behind the scenes, the hidden, what was really running my life, and the life of others. Apparently, so much is subconscious reaction. And there is a wiser, universal self who wanted me to start looking at what my subconscious programming was so that I could release twisted misperceptions of reality and experience the world through a clearer vision so as to see the deeper "truths."

This period of revelation continued not just for a few weeks but for the next few years; one mysterious contact after another with the new "wisdom energy." Constant epiphanies made me aware of the deep pleasure and the deep pain that was in the vastness of my being that I had somehow forgotten or suppressed. Out of the "Larger Me," around every corner, a miracle, a lesson of how energy is held, wasted, and how it could move in an instant to change me forever.

I started to see Thad once a month, then twice a month, then almost weekly. Every time I went in I would think this was the one time I wouldn't have an altered state, a deep epiphany, or cellular orgasm experience, but no matter what, I always did! No menstrual period, no lack of sleep, would inhibit a "deep experience" on his table. It just kept getting more frequent. I kept stepping into the unknown. Thad laughed one day as he noticed that I would consistently say the same thing after each session: "I didn't know how good I could feel in my body. I feel at home at a deeper level." It never ceased to amaze me.

It was like deep-sea diving into realms unknown. Each time I came back to the surface I couldn't possibly bring back the vast new world I encountered, but I could always manage to carry back one special pearl, a treasure from the deeper world to the surface of life.

The "void" had always been my friend, creatively. I knew this for a while, but now that "void" had the answers to things that made me fly inside spaces of time that would allow me to feel the majesty of existence: a grandness that never loses sight of all that is happening at every moment and the beauty, wisdom, and mystery that is crushingly satisfying.

Whenever I wanted to write something in the past, I would ask the absolute blackness of the "void" (primordial nothingness) --not the white light that is usually associated with God and higher consciousness--to manifest something new for an inspired and original manifestation of creativity. I would close my eyes and out of the blackness, images would fade-up and words would conjure from feeling. So I always had a good relationship to the "void."

But now I was moving into the void, the unknown itself, instead of things coming out of it. I craved the solitude to tune into the unknown. I craved the darkness as it symbolized my journey into the void. I wasn't afraid of the darkness anymore, as all of us are at times. Going into the darkness meant finding truths that were given for my whole being to grapple with and I never felt so alive! I was going into the forest of mystery, the multi-dimensions of my body/Spirit/mind.

I would stare at the night stars above after meditating many a night, crushed with beauty, the air fluttering with awareness of the unfathomable power and intelligence that created it all. The length and breadth of creation was still a mystery, but now that I had tasted a small fraction of the Life Force Energy, I was connecting to the reality that truth is so vast. I didn't think I could contain it or understand it. The Intelligence Force of Creation was real. This God Force is real. And the mystery took on a most comforting enjoyment, instead of a questioning frustration.

My longing for "THE ANSWER" was gone. It was gone, because I was living the answer unfolding. I was being fed a constant stream of realizations, some about my mental blocks, some about the nature of the higher realms in which we can function. And being in this stream I realized there was so much to know. I could hardly handle what I was being given. In starting to truly receive such energetically strong lessons from my inner teacher, the infinite grandness of the answer unfolding was apparent and humbling. Just to know this first hand was intensely gratifying.

The small bit of this intelligent power bestowed upon me in those last few months was so groundbreaking, so powerful, so loving and it was part of the fabric of all that I could see. The unanswered big life questions: life after death, our purpose in life or even our reason to exist did not matter so much anymore for I knew my ultimate fate, life, existence itself, was safe in the hands of such an intelligent force, even if I couldn't come close to comprehending it.

We are being overseen. Our journey is being created by an intelligence that has created the many universes and countless galaxies. It feels so good to have a trust in the intelligence of the Life Force Energy.

How wonderful to have a power so great, above and beyond our capacity to understand, that it will remain a mystery. That is greatness! I've never felt so humble and small and yet so special at the same time. It is one of those experiences that when you have it you realize that it was what you really were looking for all along, but you didn't know it. I was actively looking and it still caught me by a most overwhelming surprise. Aaahhh... this is what I was looking for all the time and it was more than I bargained for!

5

"And the Winner is...Sacred Sex!!! Yeah!!!"

During my next session with Thad I discussed this window into my subconscious layers that was wide open, Pandora's Box so to speak, that was consuming me, keeping me constantly processing. You don't have to physically travel to be in a foreign land; just get a passport to journey into your subconscious.

It seems that our culture, through commercial propaganda, has tried to pen us into a limited reality and awareness of ourselves. It certainly doesn't have a support system, nor does it encourage traveling into "inner dimensions" or altered states of consciousness to understand our Larger Self.

Some say that it is the way the masses can be kept as consumer zombies by the gluttonous, wealthy powers that be, continually being brainwashed that we need all these exterior ornaments, materialistic toys to make us feel beautiful, special, so that we will be loved. The fact that we are on a hamster wheel always striving for happiness through materialistic gain keeps us slaves to the money-power people. And we buy it, because no one is teaching us how to go inside to find happiness in our own cells.

Do I think there is a conspiracy with the money-power gluttons to keep us from finding God Orgasm? No. They are on the same hamster wheel, because they have no idea what pure, direct contact to bliss, their heart, is, either.

In this particular session with Thad, as the breath gained force and speedy body bliss was unleashed, I connected to a need the world has for sexual healing. And I came to realize that sacred sex is part of the answer to calm the tensions of the world. I was quoting the bible earlier, now I'll quote the hippies: "Make love not War." They just got the kind of love wrong. Direct love with the stuff that the universe is made of and is in every cell of your body was mistaken for wonton sexual debauchery that forgot the connection to the sexual union as SACRED!

As the Life Force Energy lit the sacred fire of kundalini, the juices of kundalini wet my body as sweat. I was told clearly by my "core voice" that the sexual experience of God with another person was to be healing for me, for everyone. It kept telling me:

"You need to have sex. You need to have sex while in this state and share at this energy level. It will take you deeper into places sacred and unknown. You must share this truth with someone. You must be this raw and honest with another. To experience the depths of your gift you must allow this vulnerability with others. You must only be intimate with those that know how to touch you as a sacred being."

Just as the inner kundalini teacher had stopped me from wasting my energy in a petty fight with my boyfriend, it was now teaching me about the waste and misuse of sexual energy. The energetic dialogue kept bubbling up through my cells into my consciousness.

"It's not the **quantity** of sex. It's **the quality of energy exchange** and the **directing of this energy** towards opening up to **greater self-aware-ness**. It can keep you spiraling up in your understanding and growth or it can drag you down and drain you. Opening yourself to share the sexual energy with another can be the most healing experience on earth or the most damaging. You cannot let anyone touch you in this manner who does not have an understanding of the sacred or a sincere desire to open to the sacred."

Again, for me, the only sexual object and stimulator was my own cellular energy, not Thad. It was a message about sharing and using the energy for healing and awareness. There was a new vulnerability that let me know I couldn't run around sleeping with just anyone. It was necessary to be even more selective. God was basically telling me to have tantric…SACRED SEX!

"Tantra" refers to a multitude of Hindu practices that are meant to achieve union with the universe, God. There are many tantric practices that do not have to do with sex. The West always associated tantra with sex. Only one aspect of tantra is a sex practice.

Perhaps the most satisfying existence is connecting consciously, viscerally, to the Life Force Energy in everything we do and see, as had been happening to me naturally since the kundalini awakening. There are many religious rituals and practices that are meant to remind us of the connection to God in many aspects of our lives. The Jews wear yarmulkes. The Muslims pray five times a day to keep their mind on the infinite and all knowing. The Catholics take the host and wine to symbolize our need to ingest, commune, be one with the body and blood of Christ.

It couldn't be clearer through the symbology of these rituals that all traditions have a similar message: that we must not lose remembrance of the connection with the Higher Power and that we should seek a sacred connection to our physical world at large.

Someone, once, at the early stages of these religions, was obviously having universal, cosmic-union, tantric experiences. But these ancient rituals as they are passed down, seem to become an artificial experience, not the true living experience. There is no comparison between a ritual created by someone else's understanding and experience and your own direct experience. To pass on the experience in a dry ritual will not do. This is why so much of the world is unsettled and in pain. Humans must touch their God self in their own being and then, when they touch their own body, they will feel God and the acceptance everyone craves.

Ritual will be born out of you naturally when you awaken the Life Force Energy experience, the states of communion, for its very nature is creative. Now, since I experienced the direct communion myself, I can participate, rejoice and connect through any spiritual ritual or religion since they remind me of these new sweetest, magical truths that are awakened in me.

I found that on Thad's table my body instinctively moved into positions that in and of themselves where symbolic of a state of mind, a new epiphany. It's like the position correlated with the opening and flow of a certain understanding. The position released knowledge in the cells. Again, these were spontaneous yogic movements bringing understanding of my subconscious self. I found myself doing positions I can't do normally.

I was doing a headstand on the table with my legs splayed out to the sides in Chinese splits.

So here I was, always thinking I was supposed to transcend the body, desire, and sex, but "MY GOD," the "Life Force Energy," was telling me that sex was the next step for healing and spiritual progress: sex that pushed the connection to the God-sacred-self on a tangible energy level.

Sex that wasn't only about pleasure and had no agenda, but perhaps about being more vulnerable to the entire truth of who I was. Its purpose was to feel deeper and connect deeper. If sex brings up shame or pain, cry, instead of feeling pressured to ejaculate, stay erect, or "be sexy." And in these vulnerable, open, connected states where energy moves quicker, in an instant you will be released from emotions that have held you hostage for a lifetime and you will be propelled into a bliss you have never known.

If it brings up laughter, then laugh, for the intensity of emotions and energy produces all kinds of spontaneous joy that can be the funniest thing on earth for no reason, but it's the nature of the pure joy energy itself. One time I was with a boyfriend that if I laughed during sex, he didn't like it. It threatened his idea of what "sexy" was supposed to be and threatened his sexual prowess. It had to be serious and intense to be sexy.

The sexually inspired laughter is just joy unwinding and that is one of the sexiest things I've ever felt. And if it's lusty and fun, that is part of the connecting, too. It's just that the sexual agenda of sex just for the pleasure of "cumming," getting off, must be broadened to include exploration of the subconscious and communion with our higher, expanded self and to have the experience of being touched as sacred and touching another as sacred. Real energy communion!

So there on Thad's table, in another pose that released the bliss, the kundalini God force commanded me:

"You must find your tantric love! It is the next step in your spiritual evolution."

Now, I needed to find a sacred lover. But who would understand this? A great number of men seem to be so one-track minded with their agenda of pleasure and the normal ejaculation orgasm. Everyone is so desperate for a drive-through "Jack in the Crack Cum." And many men don't understand the full body as a sexual erogenous zone. I tell people to think of the whole female body sensitivity as that of a penis and they still don't get it. They don't understand the cosmic-orgasm energy, "the secret sauce" that hides in the most unexpected crannies of the body. You never know where the energy that drives you into open kundalini abandon may be released. It could be your hand, your forearm, your psoas muscle, or your jaw into a full body orgasm.

On top of the list of qualities I looked for in a mate: smart, financially stable, honest, humorous, thoughtful, and handsome, I had to add the requisite of someone that knows how to sensually facilitate the Life Force Energy release, who would want to see God in me just as much as he would want me to play Little Bo Peep Prostitute and embody all his fantasies, and would care just as much about crying together in coitus as ejaculating. Hmm. How was I going to find my tantric lover?

In my extraordinary headstand and Chinese splits and other impossible poses, I contemplated my sexual healing and how healing sex could help so many people find a deeper connection with themselves and help them find real sexual satisfaction. I was not directing my mind toward these contemplations, but it was the poses themselves that opened me to a state where these thoughts and epiphanies bubbled up to inform me, to teach me.

I understood why it was important that tantric sexual teachers, both men and women, be Spiritually evolved, such as some that I've heard exist in India. A healer of this level must be emotionally strong enough to not be affected by all the different, strange, and traumatized energies that one would encounter in such a practice. After all, I was feeling that I needed to be more sensitive and selective as to who would I take on as a tantric lover, who I would allow to mingle in my energy field.

As I perceive the current state of spiritual evolution, I think it would be hard to find a tantric sex teacher that can open up to his or her sacred sexual experiences indiscriminately in a sex therapy scenario and not be affected by a "patient's imbalances." The need for the truly awakened "sexual healer" is there, but at present it appears to be just a fantasy. The vast majority of practicing sexual healers do not seem to be energetically advanced enough to know how to work with subconscious, subtle energy.

Once more, I lay on Thad's table to ease out of the deep altered state. Lying there, a warm, throbbing, like the strongest of the Japanese Taiko drumbeats, pulsed in my lower abdomen. It grew stronger and actually became audible to me! For real! I was actually hearing the throbbing beat of my first chakra! I was feeling and hearing my sexual chakra!!

It sounded like the deep, full, haunting, throaty chants of Tibetan monks or the humming throb of a high voltage generator that seemed to be outlining the vastness of this sex chakra dimension. It seemed to have a vibrational sonar intelligence capable of reaching out into the world to access possible sexual partners to resonate with. The humming throb let me know its strength, its power, its tangible existence, for the first time. There was a sense of vitality and pleasure that was invincible in this pulsing generator of pleasure, surging with each pulse and becoming larger and larger. Another awesome new dimension in my body awakened. The warmth and power were awesome!

* * *

I went home and felt the water from the shower as a cleansing Spirit that caressed me. I praised the water. I began to crave being connected to the water and began taking more showers, not because I felt dirty, but because I wanted to feel the soothing caresses and connection to nature's elements. I also felt that my organs needed a cooling break from the inner kundalini heat.

I called Annette to discuss my experience and confided my quest to find the right lover. I admit I wondered how Thad would be as a lover. After all, he was the catalyst for all this extravagant energy explosions. He understood how to work with the body and release energy. But it didn't feel right on other levels. It was just a thought that apparently many of his clients have, since he awakens them and there aren't many men who understand how to work with energy and the body as he does.

I was in a sexless and emotionally isolated relationship and before I found my tantric partner, I had to figure out how, or if, I was going to stay in my current relationship. Our relationship was sexless, because his financial issues emasculated him. Besides that, he was in such a bad state of mind most of the time that I thought it would be a negative experience energetically, not the healing experience I needed. So, in the current position I found myself I couldn't listen to the intuitive message to "have spiritual sex," just yet.

One night, a few months into the awakening, I went to dinner with a friend who I will call Pocahontas Dummkopf, to a popular restaurant in Hollywood called Katsuya. Double Double had bestowed that name on her, thinking her daft and spacey and considering her ethnic roots. She was a Nordic blond that resembled an older version of Bo Derek and claimed she was part Native American Indian. I had met her in one of the spiritual meditation circles I frequented before the kundalini awakening.

Pocahontas Dummkopf and I were seated at the sushi bar. Next to us at the bar happened to be Michael Bay, the famous director of "Transformers," "Pearl Harbor," etc. and a couple of his friends. I actually didn't know who he was, but Pocahontas was on full alert since she did know. We started chatting and at some point, Pocahontas Dummkopf leaned in to notify me just who we were dealing with. When we finished our dinner Michael and his friends pulled their chairs around behind us and we turned ours around so that we formed a socializing circle. Michael directed his attention to me and although I enjoyed socializing I had no interest in taking it any further since I was still in a commitment.

Suddenly, Pocahontas Dummkopf started making strange, twisted, and intense faces at me whenever our new friends were not looking, and I couldn't understand what she was trying to convey. I started to worry that she may have the onset of some neurological disorder, like Bell's palsy, where the face freezes in some contorted position or perhaps Tourette's of the face.

We all decided to move our little gathering to another location close by. My girlfriend and I went to the bathroom and she ripped into me:

"You can't talk to him while I'm trying to work my magic!" she yelled in a whisper. I was so taken aback I thought she must be joking. I sort of chuckled. She snorted with frustration at my finding it humorous.

"Are you serious? You're joking, right?" Hoping she was putting on a playful act.

"It's rude of you to keep talking to him when I was obviously giving you signals that I was interested in him," Pocahontas said with complete entitlement.

"Ooooh! So that's what all those strange faces were about? No. I had no clue what the hell was going on with you," I said in continued disbelief.

"Yes. I need him to focus on me when I do my spells on him to draw him to me," she continued, her voice softening into a cutesy tone once she realized I was unaware what her facial contortions had meant. "I guess you didn't know, so I won't be mad at you."

"Look, first of all I'm in a relationship and I have no interest in this guy. And secondly, it's up to the natural feeling of a person as to who they like and you can't change that. You can't put spells on people to like you more than someone else," I said demoralized that I was finding out my friend was a desperate little nut job.

"Oh, you just don't know what I can do. I've done it before and it works...if no one interferes," she insisted with total conviction.

"Look, I'm not interested in Michael, but I'm not going to sit around and not say anything at a social gathering. I'm here to enjoy a social night out and have fun," I said. I didn't know this girl too well, but was starting to realize she was loony and the worst kind of loon at that, a bossy one!

What was she doing thinking she could put a "spell" on Michael? Who the hell did Pocahontas Dummkopf think she was? She better work some kind of something, because he was obviously not into her. At the next stop, I made sure to let her sit next to him. The evening became boring since I had to watch my step around Michael and watch my looney friend's face to see if it would melt into some painful expression to signal me of some more of her jealousy.

I got home at 2 in the morning as my girlfriend and I had a little discussion to straighten things out between us after the socializing with Michael and friends. Double Double with Cheese was nowhere to be found!

"Double Double where are you?" I called out as I went from room to room.

There was no response. Silence. I kind of thought he may be hiding and went around in a playful manner looking as if it was a game of hide and seek.

"Double Double, I'm going to find you and when I do..." I stopped calling out to him mid-sentence when I finally noticed a letter left on the bed.

"Suraya: You didn't come home or call me to let me know you were coming late so I assume you must have met someone else. If you did, I understand. I know how difficult it has been to be around me and how horrible it must be to be around my bad moods. I know I've been horrible company and I know I've neglected you, so I don't blame you. I wish you the best with whomever you have met. You deserve better. I love you too much for you to come home to me when you've been with another man so I'm staying in a hotel for the night."

I called him instantly and he answered. I insisted that he come home convincing him that nothing happened. Double Double came back for the night with relief and love in his eyes, but we both knew it was over.

I hadn't met anyone, nor was I looking, yet, nor could I with my melting Wicked Witch of the West face friend, but it was a relief to see that he understood how things could obviously not go on the way they were. I guess I was waiting for him to understand. He moved out to a place of his own. We continued to see each other for a short period in this new living situation and then broke up. Luckily, the break-up was smooth and natural, no more big drama. My fears that the project we were working on together would go belly up or suffer from my not being a priority in his life were unfounded. We continued to work together for some time, amicably. Pocahontas Dummkopf's love spell may not have worked on Michael Bay, but that night full of her desperate, bogus magic did free me from the spell of a loveless relationship.

The time had finally come for me to "go forth and mingle," to find my tantric sex partner!

6
"Deepening the Practice"

Thad started to share the other aspects of his process to awaken energy awareness by encouraging me to partake in his yoga class and also suggested that I go see a very cutting-edge nutritionist to detoxify. I had done yoga years ago and thought it was so boring, that if the invitation had not come from this most wicked master of energy, I would not have been enticed.

Thad explained to me that the yoga and the processes of detoxifying my body would deepen my ability to experience and move the Life Force Energy. It was part of his program called "Rule of Four." The Rule of Four practice entails finding out which sequence of therapy modalities pertains to each individual to unlock the defense mechanisms that prevent access to the unconscious and allows communion with the "Core Self," the authentic self, the undefended heart that is the source of love, endless energy and intuitive wisdom.

To get to the core self you must access the subconscious where one's greatest pleasures, traumas, and God-self lie locked away. The process refers to the assessment which has four possible reasons for which a person has blocked the connection and experience of the Life Force Energy: 1) emotional trauma and stresses, 2) physical trauma from injuries and surgeries, 3) tightness/lack of flexibility, and 4) toxicity due to diet and environmental causes.

The Rule of Four assessment starts with emotional traumas and Thad's bodywork unlocks the emotional traumas held as tension and pain in the body. If the trauma is too severe the client will not open up until he does some psychiatric work. Thad then will send the client to an appropriate therapist for the condition before he continues to work with them.

If someone doesn't have a good sense of self, a healthy ego, they may not feel safe exploring "the unknown" that is the subconscious, the cosmic self and peak-altered experiences. Then the experience may be too frightening. It may just add to the insecurity the person feels in the world. You must have the strength of courage to step out of your "box" and that comes with at least a semi-solid, healthy ego.

The second and third rules that must be assessed for blocks to communicate with the core are related to the body. If a person is either too physically tight and pained due to lack of flexibility or as the result of an accident, where the body is fused uncomfortably by scar tissue or out of alignment, then Thad will send clients to do yoga or physical therapy for a few months before he starts working with them.

The fourth rule focuses on nutrition and toxicity. Again, Thad recommends some time-honored detoxifying programs, liver cleanses and vitamin supplements. However, he often sends people to nutritionists for more severe cases of physical ailments.

My friend Fiona had been working with Thad's program of body-work and yoga for a year, but still she was not experiencing moving her Life Force Energy and the pleasure that goes with it. She would watch the demonstrations in his classes and long for the waves of ecstasy that she watched others open up to.

And lo and behold, after she did serious detoxifying and went on a diet specific to her needs, the energy moved through her in convulsive pleasure waves at the slightest trigger. It could be as simple as taking a naked bath in a river and letting the water flow over her and I witnessed her quiver and undulate in electric waves of pleasure. She was like an energy conduit from then on.

I reluctantly went to Thad's yoga class. It was one of those classes where the heat is cranked up intentionally to make the muscles elastic. Now that I had experienced the kundalini sweat, the sweat in class was cleansing emotionally and melted my body open. The more I melted physically, the more I opened up to emotional bliss. This was not like any other yoga class I had taken.

Thad, the mix master, played the tribal, soulful, and etheric music that he played in his bodywork to coax the energy in the cells to move. All throughout the class he spoke and inspired with beautiful quotes of great poets that also had brushes with the Divine, like Rumi, Whitman, and Emerson. He incorporated the yoga breath of two quick exhales and the class was energetically off to the races.

"The minute I heard my first love story, I started looking for you, not knowing how blind that was. Lovers don't finally meet somewhere, they're in each other all along"

- Rumi

Someone in the corner of the class started to breathe heavily and then began to make liberating ecstatic sounds. Later in the class someone would be weeping out the pain of the day, or perhaps of a lifetime. Thad would encourage everyone to be present with whatever emotion was there in the moment and allow it to be. The magic was apparently in the utter acceptance of the full range of human emotions and in being present with it.

"Out beyond the ideas of wrongdoing and right doing there is a field. I will meet you there."

- Rumi

"When the soul lies down in the grass the world is too full to talk about ideas, language, even the phrase *each other* doesn't make sense."

- Rumi

When allowing the floodgates of one's humanity to open through this emotional acceptance, divinity starts to come to life and take shape. It is ALL O.K. The great sadness is bearable and the great pleasure is allowed. As I relished in my humanity in these classes I began to see that I had dumbed myself down by not allowing myself to feel the fullness of these emotions. There is so much to learn, so much intelligence through the "feeling" versus the intellectual aspect of self. Again, it is the body wisdom that we have cut ourselves off from through cultural ignorance, through family ignorance and inherited traumas from parent to child.

"You were born with wings. Why do you prefer to crawl through life?"

- Rumi

And then suddenly, within the structure of Thad's yoga class moving together as a whole, someone would take off in his or her own inspired *asana* (yoga pose), that worked as an emotional doorway and physical release. Thad was allowing us to realize that, within the structure, we always needed to listen to the spontaneous wisdom that springs up from our body, our cellular guide telling us how to unwind the stresses and transport us into greater awareness, feeling and comfort in our body. His classes were a tribal ritual where people were allowed to explore the depth of human emotion and trance.

Thad always tells the story that he believes that yoga is a "living practice." He envisions that yoga was created by *sadhus*, God seekers in India, in caves where they managed to tap into the Life Force Energy and it is the energy that moved them in these spontaneous positions that we call yoga *asanas*.

It's not about a perfect static pose. Each person's perfection of a pose will look different according to the person's physical need. It is about learning to unleash the Life Force Energy to guide you into the poses that will take you deeper into awareness of the self.

It is here in Thad's class that my relation to pain, emotionally and physically, was changing. It was much more palatable and welcome, not something to be so scared of, avoided, since right on the other side of the tightly held block, was pleasure. I was becoming the smiling, naturally psychedelic Cheshire cat he was, myself. I have learned that one of the great secrets to Thad's work is learning to accept the pain, move into the pain, and through it. When you are so afraid of the pain and avoid it, you cannot reclaim the bliss that is your "Whole Self" and a block is created.

The edge of pain in a stretching pose began to have a sense of pleasure and curiosity to it, because you never knew what inner experience or emotion it would evoke. I was able to use my two quick yoga breaths and move the energy to release the tension and go further in the stretch. Then the new depths of release in the pose would open the Kundalini flow and I was in heated bliss.

When the Life Force Energy was released, I could go even deeper, melting into the stretch--and the ecstasy of the body would dance in my cells and move me intuitively to greater bliss and greater stretch and inner intuitive wisdom would start to rise up to the surface and converse with me. I would step out of sync with the set class and synchronize with my inner teacher that would intuitively drive me into a spontaneous backbend where my head, upside down, would be shaking like a mad woman in release and ecstasy. It actually looked somewhat like the scene from the Exorcist where she is walking down the steps in a backbend while her head spun around in circles. I was in the kundalini fire. This is the spontaneous movement practice that invented yoga.

At the end of class I sat outside the entrance of the yoga studio toweling myself off on a cushiony seat as I was drenched in a most satisfying sweat, so relaxed, so pleased. I watched as the other students emerged from their melting experience.

Then it dawned on me that I was single now and starting to look for my tantric partner was a good idea, not like a cat ready to pounce, but with one eye open to the world of men as I still let the dust settle from my breakup, curious to see what this world of Thad's yoga may offer in terms of enlightened men. I thought that a man from Thad's class would be primed and ready and have an understanding of this most sacred energy opening and altered-states sex my being longed for, as a new kind of nourishment that I needed to evolve, right?

As far as finding a tantric partner in Thad's class there was no one of interest to me or to whom I was remotely attracted.

They kept coming out one after another, and to my astonishment there was always one more person to emerge seemingly from nowhere. It was like a disconcerting yet comical attempt to break a world record of the greatest number of midgets fit into a mini cooper as the parade of students to pop out of that small room continued. All smiling, satisfied, as one after another they spilled out, all women, except for three men! Only one cute, heterosexual, my friend Lafer, and the rest were gay. Unless I was going to be lesbian, I realized this wasn't a good pool of suitors. A sharp reminder that this world of spirituality seems to consist primarily of women.

I was so satisfied within my being at this point, I couldn't bring myself to fret or worry, but I did realize that the practicality of finding my tantric partner would not be as easy as I thought. But I had to believe that the fates gave me this most miraculous opening and longing to grow in all ways and that my sexual growth would be taken care of as well. It just may not be in an obvious or logical place, such as in a yoga class or spiritual community, but in a unique and most unexpected person that would continue to confirm that my life is to be a most blessed string of gifts that come as unexpected surprises. I said to myself: "My tantric lover will come!"

7

"Everyday Life"

The ocean view was spectacular from my gym, which is right across from the beach. The entire side of the gym that faces out to the ocean is all glass walls from floor to ceiling. It's a down-to-earth hometown vibe. It really has a small club feel, not the usual pick-up place for singles that a gym can often be. Everyone is friendly and I have friends of all ages there.

I walked through the entrance and waved to people I know as I passed the café.

"Hey Leonidas!" I yelled out to my friend, a geneticist at UCLA and soccer buff extraordinaire. He's always upbeat and works out to a profuse sweat. He always speaks so lovingly about his wife and love of his life and his two daughters. He seems like a truly happy man.

"Hey Suraya!"

"Hey Simone!" I called out to another friendly face. Simone is one of the gym's masseuses from whom I get a massage occasionally. She is one of the few women strong enough to give me the kind of deep tissue massage I like. We've become friendly over time.

"Hey Suraya! I have a cancellation this afternoon if you want to take the slot."

"No, not today, no time, but I need to come in soon," I replied

"Hey Craig." I said as I went up to the café food counter next to Craig chowing down a meal. I always catch Craig nabbing a meal, which is not surprising as he is one of those perpetual bachelors.

"Hi Suraya! You're looking good today."

"Thanks! You too, but you look a bit tired. You've been surfing? I heard the waves have been crazy big," I said.

"Oh, my God you have no idea. I can surf some good waves, but these are too big for me. I got a bit thrashed and beaten down by them. You have to be careful with storm waves like these, they can be dangerous."

"Well, rest up. I'm going to get to my workout."

"Nice seeing you as always, Suraya."

I walked up the steps to the weight floor and started to stretch my calves on a calf-stretch incline next to the railing that overlooked the stairs and the gym.

"Hey Suraya!" I heard Buddy, one of my young friends from the gym, yell out from the railing on the other side of the stairwell. Seventeen-year-old Buddy was training to be a dead-weight lifter. I had known him since he was fifteen and had watched him grow from a normal looking muscular teen into a tall, overly inflated, bulky deadweight lifter. He actually had purposely put on a lot of fat along with his new muscles; apparently the extra fat is needed for deadweight lifting. He always had a jug, not just a bottle, of a fluorescent green energy drink that looked like Incredible Hulk Juice that he hauled around the gym with him.

"Hey, hey, hey! How was your date with the new girl?" I asked. Buddy had recently broken up with his first girlfriend. They had gone out for two years so this was the first time he was back in the dating pool.

"I ended it. Never asked her out."

"Why not? You were so excited."

"I got scared."

"You? Scared! You're so outgoing. What are you talking about?"

"I know. But girls today don't like muscular guys like me. They like the skinny guys. The musician types."

"That's not true. There are a lot of girls that will love the muscly look. You should've at least tried," I attempted, encouraging his mutant teenage mind--as all teens seem to have mutant brains that tend to deduce things in a more extreme and dramatic manner than is usually true.

"Yeah, I know," he agreed sheepishly.

"You know maybe the girls like the musician types because they write music and they think that is romantic. Music is emotion. It appeals to their emotional side."

"Yeah, I'm not romantic at all. Ha! No way! Ha! Me romantic? That would be ridiculous," he said as if romance was distasteful and completely foreign.

I had found myself wanting to mentor some of the young men at the gym about love, romance and sex. They always wanted to chat with me so I felt I had their ear, interest, and respect so I had an in. Looking after their growth I felt like a den mother, protective, responsible to try to steer them in a direction that would help them mature in a well- rounded way sexually. They seemed at such a loss sometimes. A good word from a mature woman at the right time perhaps would plant a seed to help them be happy and make their lover even happier in the future.

"You're not romantic? Why not?" I asked astounded.

"I don't know. I'm just not. And it's like a waste of time. I mean I did take my ex-girlfriend to dinner and buy her a present and card for

Valentine's, but romantic like talking romantic or writing romantic things or doing romantic surprises no, I don't do those things. I just go for the sex."

"What do you do, then? You just go up to a girl, club her on the head and drag her away by the hair, caveman style?" I teased.

"No of course not!" He laughed. "I don't club anyone on the head. I'm not a brute."

"I'm just teasing. I know you don't club people. It's just the way you talk you sound a little one-dimensional," I said. "You want to be a good lover, don't you?"

"Yes of course."

"Well, being a great lover means including as many senses into a shared experience as you can to create a heightened sensuality – that is romantic! Some of the best sex is super sexual and romantic at the same time."

"I have no idea what you're talking about" he chuckled, feeling foolish and ignorant, but self-effacing enough to find the humor in his youthful male cluelessness.

"I feel I can share some of my personal experience to give you an example," the den mother in me said.

"Here is a story that is a perfect example" I began, as if offering a great tale of wisdom. "One of my first boyfriends gave me one of the most amazing experiences. He was attending university and was coming over super late one night after an intense day of study. He came in through the backyard sliding door into the living room and took me right over to the dining room and lay me on the dining room table and we started to have sex. Right when I was reaching an orgasm, I felt this waft of amazing flower fragrance and felt something velvety soft falling on my face and body. I opened up my eyes to see he was drizzling flower petals all my body. The surprise and the smell and the feel of the flowers intensified the whole orgasmic experience. It was sexy, hot! The intermingling of his masculine "take charge" attitude of taking me with great authority to do it on the dining room table, mixed with the beautiful, delicate creative touch of the petals, made it both exquisitely lusty and romantic! Unforgettable!"

"Wow! That's a lot of work!" He blurted out innocently and we both bust up laughing.

"You don't do it every time, silly. You do it every now and then...that is if you care to be a great lover," I replied. I saw another gym goer's face smile as they overheard the conversation and I realized we were speaking for all to hear on the weight floor since we had to talk loud enough to be heard across the stairwell. But there was nothing to hide and maybe our conversation would inspire some people not to need to suddenly run to a corner and share in whispers. Out in the open for all I say.

"That's really amazing he did that for you. So thoughtful! I would never think of that. I don't know if I want to be *that* good of a lover." We laughed again as I shook my head at the possible hopelessness of it all.

"Be a creative, thoughtful lover. Have fun with it as if it's a game of how to conjure up the greatest surprise for your lover. You create memorable moments like that and the girls will value you way more than the diamonds and pearls you give them."

"Well, they aren't going to be getting diamonds and pearls from me. Unless they are cheap ones from Zale's or fake ones like cubic zirconia." We busted up laughing again.

"I'm giving you pearls of wisdom here."

"I totally appreciate it. Tell me some more stories," he said genuinely interested, resisting a slight smirk rising up out of one side of his mouth like the cat that was plotting on eating the bird. "I want to learn to be a good lover and I need some ideas because they don't come to me."

"Ha, ha! O.K…Hmmm, let me think. Ah, yes! Here is another good example of how sex and romance can meet. I opened my blinds on Valentine's Day to a find painting in the yard that my boyfriend painted of me. The painting was a depiction of him handing me a dozen roses as I slept naked. Next to the painting were a dozen roses in a vase and a card. I was so impressed and flattered as I wondered how he found the time to paint it while he was so busy with graduate school. I could feel the inspiration he felt in our love. "

"That's super romantic, but where's the sex part? Is that a girl thing that romance is sexy or something?" he complained.

"Well, I was naked in the painting, which was erotic, but the *sex part,* as you put it, was in the story. He had a huge workload, so to paint it he had to stay up late several nights and hardly slept a few nights to create this personally inspired work of art. That is passion. Passion is sexy. Not only that, but he was so aroused painting it, even with the lack of sleep he irresistibly masturbated and came on the painting seven times during its creation. He said the energy of his love and passion were literally immortalized in the painting with his essence."

"He came on the painting seven times? Really? Or is that a joke?"

"Really, it's a true story."

"That's gross! And hot at the same time!" he exclaimed and we both busted up laughing, again.

"Yeah, I agree it's a bit of both, but if you're in love with someone and the sex is amazing it's totally hot!" I said and he listened intently.

"Could you see the cum on the painting?" he asked with a few uncomfortable ticks that twinged out of his face and he swallowed hard.

"No, you couldn't see the cum. He mixed it in with the brushstrokes," I replied.

"Seven times! That must have messed up the painting a few times. That's a lot of brushstrokes!" he joked. "I've never been inspired by anyone like that! I can only draw stick figures so they'd be disappointed anyway."

"Everyone has to find their range of what is sexy and what is gross. I found it incredibly sexy and romantic. He created a passionate, sexy, romantic memory that will last forever. I will always keep the painting. Whatever happens in life I will know that I was wildly and passionately loved and desired if I inspired such a grand gesture."

"Can I see it? I want to see it…out of a sick curiosity, but I don't want to touch it! Yeech!" he said, making me laugh so hard I was practically crying.

"Sure you can see it. Maybe I'll show it to you someday. It's not the best likeness, but it's cute and the meaning is there," I agreed.

"So what other ideas do you have? I need more ideas, because I'm stupid and I may not do those big dramatic gestures," he said, pushing for more.

"No, I think you've had enough wisdom for today," I said, as we continued to laugh at the ridiculousness of the romantic sex lesson at the gym. "But I will leave you with one last tidbit," I added, always overflowing with the spirit of wanting to inspire better lovers in the world: "He kissed me once outside in my yard and mid-kiss suddenly he swung me around and said "I want you to have the view of the full moon while we kiss." He continued to kiss me deeply and every time my eyes fluttered open from the trance great kissing can produce, I had the view of the full moon over his shoulder. Now you can do that one, right?"

"That's a good one, too. Yeah, I could do that one. I don't know if I'll ever be romantic. I need help," he said giddy with the humor of the subject matter and the realization that he was romantically impaired. "It's as if I wasn't born with an arm or something and have to do it with my foot so I can't do it as well as other people can," he said as we continued our mutual laughter.

"Having the right partner to inspire you does help the creative juices," I encouraged.

"You're like the Martha Stewart or the Oprah Winfrey of sex. You should charge to give sexy romantic ideas for idiots like me," he complimented.

"Yeah, true. You never know." I mused at all the things that were unfolding in my life and how the trajectory of my life was taking a surprising new direction with the awakening I was going through. "Got to go! Now ask that girl out!"

"Maybe. See you later!" Buddy walked away with great effort, as his overly-massive body seemed to produce a resistance to normal movement as if he was pushing through a thick swamp as he lumbered away.

"Remember, the more senses you can include in the experience, the better, if you want to be a great lover," I called out as I descended the stairs to leave.

It was nice to try and enlighten a friend to expand his sexual possibilities to include romance. I must sound like a hedonist in ways. Yes, I am a hedonist, a hedonist with heart. We must show each other how to hold life's meaningful moments so preciously in the center of our being, for they are a well to drink from throughout the years. These memories have kept me in awe and peace. They will whisper to me from time to time, "You have been truly loved! You have been adored!"

What does love look like to you? Is it petals during orgasm? Is it paintings colored by your lover's cum? In between the moments of sorrow, strife, boredom, and burden, we must insist on taking every chance we get to create scintillating memories that reverberate in a lover's heart and may even echo on after the body has passed into the feeling universe. There is no better way than love expressed from the imagination of the heart and the lustful forces that twist and forge us in the heat of divine passion and playfulness, into beings that, in the very way we move through life, the way we walk, the way we talk, and the way we laugh, easily pronounce to the world that we know love. And in knowing we are loved, we become artful visual and vibrational templates that, without even trying, begin the awakening of love potential in each other.

Once I was lost, absorbed in a most sensual kissing session with a lover on the corner of a street. We were on our way somewhere about to cross the street and suddenly we realized we had actually reached our destination on that very street corner, kissing. Then a woman's voice cut into our world of two, "Oh, that's so beautiful! What you're doing is preventing rape somewhere in the world today. Keep doing it!"

We see love and that's how we learn to love!

Now, with all my encouraging memories from the past that I imparted as inspiration to help the young lovers of the world, I had to turn the spotlight back on myself. I had to heed the message from the Life Force Energy and dare to find my tantric lover, the next step for me on this path of awakening into divine love.

I went through one of my usual weight routines. After my squat sets I started to stretch on the squat bar and do my yogic breaths. Right there in the middle of muscle central the waves of kundalini heat released me into bliss. I started to moan in a low rumbling with the pleasure that took me to a new edge. I was finding it easier and easier to connect with and stimulate this amazing force in daily activities. Stretching (yoga), meditation, being in nature, and bodywork became doors into peak, altered states of perception and now apparently, even at the gym! This Life Force was fanning out into my life through these mediums and the mystery of life's endless power seemed present practically at all times.

I kept the moaning low so as not to tip anyone off that I was having a spiritual/physical ecstasy. I wasn't ready to share this spontaneous experience with my young gym friend even though it is probably the kind of experience that would be most important to share in regards to the pleasure of spirituality and the potential of sexual pleasure seeping out into every day, none-sexual activities in subtle ways, just the pleasure of one's own Life Force Energy, the pleasure of being Alive in a body!

What a most delicious and full inner life was unfolding in my everyday life from this atomic energy explosion of the Kundalini awakening. I was in on the most precious of secrets. A mystical spring popped open in my being that was bathing my mundane life in magic and quenching my being from a thirst I didn't even know I had all these years.

"Hola Suraya!" I heard the thick Hispanic accent of my friend Marita, an older Colombian woman in her fifties, say. With her short bob with bangs, her black Indian hair, she had that sheen that reflected light. She was a dark skinned, fine-featured woman, thin and vibrant.

"Hi Marita." I said and gave her a hug. She hugged me tighter.

"Oh, how is my Suraya doing? Are you OK, not hurting too much from the break-up?" she said, truly sympathetic. Even after we pulled out of the hug, she held onto my arms warmly, concerned.

"I'm fine. You're so sweet, but I was not heartbroken. It was a long time coming. One of those situations where I've not been feeling good in the relationship for a while, so it's more of a relief," I assured my sweet friend. Being Hispanic myself, I have a certain fondness for my Latino friends with whom I have a chance to chat in Spanish. It's comforting to me.

"Yes! That's the good attitude. *Eso!* No man is worth it if he doesn't treat you right. Better be without him. Wait until you find the right one, like

I did. My first husband was horrible. He cheated on me all the time and it was hard to leave him, because I have three children with him, but I did. No, it's not worth living in pain or with someone where the love is not good. And look at me now. I'm with the love of my life. You know he pursued me hard. I was so guarded with men after the bad experience with my husband, I was not easy and very aloof, but he was persistent. And he is the best thing in my life. He raised my three children, not their father. I don't know what I would do without him," she said gushing, like a romance *novela* of "true love."

"Yeah, he's a good guy. I can see how dedicated he is to you."

"Don't worry. You'll meet someone wonderful. You deserve the best. You are so beautiful and smart and you have such a good heart."

"I'm not worried. I just have to wait for the right one as you said. I just had a very deep spiritual experience and I feel I want someone with whom I can connect on a spiritual/sexual level." I explained.

"Oohhh, yesss! My beautiful Suraya is so spiritual! I love it! Yes! That would be perfect! You know I'm very spiritual too. You are such a good girl. You deserve the best! In fact, I think I know someone for you," she said with such enthusiasm, I thought we were on stage in a play and she had to over-project for the large auditorium.

"Wow! You do? That would be quick if I meet someone right now."

"Are you open to the idea? I will introduce you. He is at this gym," she said conspiratorially. "Let me see if he is here now," she said, as she craned her head around looking at the far corners and crannies of the gym. "He is not here."

"Yes. Sure. I trust you have good taste. Who is it?"

"I can't remember his name right now. Oh, it's on the tip of my tongue," she said with a constipated, knitted brow in concentration. "I can't remember. But he is cute and very funny. Can I tell him about you?" she asked almost pleading.

"Yes, of course. I'm open, I'm open."

"Good! I will let you know or I will tell you to come so I can point him out and introduce you."

"Great! You're so sweet!"

"Eres tan linda! Y espiritual. You're so beautiful and spiritual. You deserve the best," she said, kissing me on the cheek. "I need to go meet my beautiful man downstairs. Bye my Suraya. *Adiós, mi linda!*" she said blowing a few kisses to me as she left. I blew a few back, laughing at the sweetness of our exchange and thinking how cute and expressive she was.

I decided that I should paint my room as part of the "out with the old, in with the new" ritual cleansing process, clearing the energy of my breakup. They say many people change their hairstyle or hair color after a major breakup, but I had done that once before and practically ruined my hair as I went from blond to black to blond to red so I wasn't going to be screwing around with my crowning glory anymore.

I've always had this fantasy that I would one day take a year off and build my own house with a construction crew. I fantasized about not only personally designing my house but imbuing my home with the love and care of using my hands. I also wanted to gain confidence in the arena of practical survival. I've always wanted to know if I had the basic skills to survive in the wilderness, such as home building, hunting, and foraging. There is a confidence and freedom in that kind of basic survival knowledge. In preparation for this fantasy of building my house someday I like to dabble in handy work around the house every now and again. So instead of hiring painters, as I have in the past, I decided I was going to paint my room myself. How hard could it be?

I bought the same cream color paint that covered the walls of my bedroom and with a few pointers from my mother, started what was going to be the best, fastest and easiest paint job ever and a new accomplishment.

The first day I painted had passed in a snap and I'd only done one wall in a sixteen by sixteen room. Did I take too many breaks? No. Well, first day I had to deal with prep and you can always chuck it up to a learning curve. "It will go faster tomorrow and I'll finish up," I thought to myself.

"Litty, how are you doing in here?" My mother came in to check on the painting as I was sitting atop the ladder contemplating my job and laying one last brush stroke. "Oh, you have a lot to do still," she said laughing. "I thought you'd be done by now. You're taking too long."

"I know. I thought I'd be done too. Don't laugh," I said as I began to laugh through my spent body prompting her to laugh harder. "I didn't think it would be so hard."

"Look at her on the top of the ladder, working so hard," she said in a cutesy voice as if humoring a child. In her mocking tone and a twinkle in her eye I could feel and hear her admiring my gumption as always and enjoying my stupidity at the same time. "It shouldn't be so hard. You're making it too hard. You can't be so meticulous. I'm going to show you the strokes to do it faster," she said and picked up the roller and attached it to a long stick and demonstrated a few strokes that covered much more wall terrain.

"Ok. Ok. I see. I get it. I've had it for today. I need to get down from here and eat," I said, slumping down the ladder as my mom chuckled at me. I resisted asking her to help. I wanted to do it myself.

Then the next day went by and I had finished two more walls, but I still did not finish! I started at that last wall late in the night thinking "I just can't do it. I have to finish tomorrow. Damn it! Blasted it! I need my sleep."

Then the third day I finished the last wall! Yes!! I took a step back to look at my prodigious job and I saw some blotchiness. How could I have missed spots after meticulously taking three days to paint one room? Had I gone into some strange meditation where I had lost track of time for hours and not painted as much as I had thought? No, my meditations were about an hour a day. I ate meals quickly. I hadn't had some spiritual, mystical experience with each brush stroke that made me loose myself for an inordinate amount of time because I discovered a microscopic Dr. Seuss world of unimaginable wonder, like an overly stoned or hallucinating teenager. Was I simply that bad at painting?

"Oh, you look like you're finally done." My mother peeked her head in again just as I was assessing my final job. "Oh!" she exclaimed then put her hand on her mouth.

"What? What do you see? You can spit it out."

"I just saw a little spot you missed there." She so delicately presented her critique.

"Mom, how long has it taken you to paint a room?" I asked.

"No more than a day, sometimes just a few hours. How long has it taken you?" She asked.

"You know I've been at this three days and it doesn't even look right," I said and my mother busted up laughing.

"Three days? Oh, I see a few more spots that you missed."

"I can't take it anymore. I've had it. I'm calling a painter to do it over from scratch," I said exasperated. "After all this and I didn't even notice I didn't like the color the whole time. I kept thinking it would look different when I was done."

"Yes, I would say that is your best bet," she said still reveling in laughter over my ordeal. "Whatever it costs, you should spend the money, because you can't waste any more time on this."

One thing about my family is that we always laugh about everything including each other's mishaps. If I slipped on a banana peel it would be most humorous for them, after they had been assured that I was not injured of course. Even if I were a little bruised, they'd be cracking up. Having such a ready wit in a family dynamic is a great gift. It has taught me to laugh at myself a great deal, but I've noticed that others that were not raised with this kind of ready humor often are offended if you laugh when they slip on that banana peel.

I called the professional painter and they came and painted the whole room in 2 hours perfectly! A kick in the teeth to my survival skills. Well, actually if I had to build a shelter in the wilderness I guess it may not be a priority to paint it. Ha!

Well, now my room was ritually, energetically cleansed from the last relationship, another step readying myself to move on.

8

"The Clown and The Crucifixion"

How do you choose a sacred-sex partner? What do you look for to qualify this most precious position? Did I want it to be in a committed relationship? Did I want a boyfriend? These are the questions I began to mull over.

After all, I felt that after the deep and liberating experiences I had, I was ready for the most emotionally honest, loving, sexually charged relationship of my life. But coming out of a very tense relationship, I wasn't sure I wanted to jump back into another one so fast. I was ready for a new level of connecting that I wasn't aware existed. I felt this might be the time to have the most vibrant relationship of my life or at least the most groundbreaking sexual God experiences of my life. I was willing to dare to seek this fulfillment. But how?

I called Annette, my physical therapist/turned confidant in this strange new path that she had sent me on, to ask her advice as to my plight to find a tantric partner. I was hoping she would know someone, but she didn't seem to have any energetically gifted tantric men in her stable of friends and acquaintances.

I was at a loss as to how to go about this process of finding someone to explore these highly energetic sex and full-body orgasms that catapulted me into vulnerable altered states of awareness. How to put the word out and not get a bunch of weirdoes?

I mean, the odds are most men would say that they were interested on principle. They would just want to get laid or add to their repertoire of kink. "Oh…something new!"

I've been surprised at the stories my male friends have shared with me about their "openness" in the experimentation department. Like my dear friend that would humor his girlfriend's fetish of wanting him to watch her and her friends screw her large German Shepherd. Enough said, right? Well, except that when my friend wanted to have sex with his girlfriend, the dog would be pawing at the door feverishly in jealousy. They'd have to lock the dog out of the room or the dog would attack him. Or my friend whose girlfriend had such a strong rape fantasy that she would want them to meet at a designated lawn in a residential area and he would have to jump and aggressively rape her. He would tear her clothes to shreds and then according to her pre-agreed upon direction leave her on the lawn to find her way back home so she could feel the sense of being a victim to the core. The things my friends confess to me. *Oy vey*!

One day I was at the doctor's office getting a vitamin I.V. for a cold I was fighting. There were several Lazy Boy Recliners set in a circle in a room and different people sitting together to receive their specific vitamin cocktail; some for a serious illness like cancer, others for heavy metal poisoning, yet others for work-related stresses or drugs. The latter is usually the problem of famous entertainment folk who are run down from substance excesses and the physical demands of filming or touring.

I've met some very interesting characters in that room, to name a few: James Earl Jones, Anthony Keedis, Flee, Bob Hope's illegitimate son, the president of the ACLU. He gave me a bunch of his magazines in gratitude for stories that I shared in that health way station where people of interesting walks of life congregated in the pursuit of wellness.

On this particular dopy nose-congestion day I was sitting quietly in my Lazy Boy when a very famous comedian came in to visit with a friend receiving an I.V. He had received many Emmy's for his TV shows, but I didn't know who he was because I was too young when his show was a hit. He had a monkey-like face and looked like someone I knew, but who was he?

Well, his piercing eyes flashed big when he saw me and he kept glancing over. Then suddenly he came over toward my Lazy Boy recliner. Then I remembered who he looked like! It was the Grinch from Dr. Seuss The Grinch Who Stole Christmas!"

"You look pretty healthy. What's wrong with you? Is it serious?" he asked.

"You're pretty forward. What if I'm dying and I've got to explain it to the likes of you?" I said and laughed. He looked like he didn't know how to respond. "But no, I'm not dying. I just have a flu."

"You scared me for a second," he said and sat in the chair next to me and reached over and grabbed my boot and held my foot in his hand. "I was worried that maybe I had stuck my foot in my mouth."

"No, but by the way you're grabbing my foot, I'm afraid you want to stick my foot in your mouth," I retorted, and he finally laughed.

We started to talk and I guess my sarcastic, saucy sense of humor pulled him in and before I knew it he was asking for my number. A friend of mine said that he must have wanted to touch me anyway he could, even if that meant grabbing my boot, dirty sole and all. Hey, any man willing to humble himself to grab your dirty boot deserves a try.

I went to visit with this comedian at his comfortable Santa Fe-style home in Brentwood. Let's call him "Lazy Boy," like the recliner I was sitting on when I met him. On our first visit--I wouldn't call it a date--we just talked.

"There is something different about you. You exude this peace and calm that has eluded me my whole life. You seem content," Lazy Boy said and I couldn't believe he launched into all his problems right of the bat.

"I've just had a big spiritual opening, a kundalini opening," I said.

"Kundalini! I do kundalini yoga. But I don't feel anything from it. I bet you would be a better teacher to help me start to experience things than my teacher."

"I guarantee you that what she does and what I would do are totally different," I said as I went into a detailed telling of my kundalini explosion sexual build up, full-body orgasm, bliss and all.

"I knew you would be better than my kundalini teacher. I want to have that! Why do those experiences come to others and not to me?"

"If you really want to explore what has led me to my current experiences you should have some sessions with Thad."

"You don't know the pain I've been in my whole life," he said launching into his life story of pain as he clenched his chest. "You know, it wasn't easy for me to make it. Some people are so gifted and comedy is so natural to them. I had to work at it. I bombed at so many clubs for years. You can't imagine the sheer will it took to keep going. And I would just be by myself and keep working on my craft. I was so lonely. And now even with all my success, I'm still sooo lonely!"

"It's so cliché, but so true. Here we are sitting in your gorgeous backyard of your six-million-dollar home. You've reached the pinnacle of success possible in a comedian's career and you're rich. Whereas I have none of that, yet, and I'm so happy and you're not. It really shows you it's all in the heart. I feel the joy, the wealth, the pleasure wash through me all the time for no reason at all. I feel sorry for you."

"I'm so petrified that I will never be able to open my heart, fully, before I die. I am so afraid I will never be able to love someone unless I open my heart," he said so impotently. His face looked like one of those tormented humans in medieval depictions of the tortures of hell. "I think you can help me open my heart."

It left such an impression on me as to where happiness lies. You can have everything you want, but not what you really need–an open heart!

He suddenly started to make some crazy-ass faces that looked like Jim Carey on PCP.

"Are you ok? Should I call an ambulance?" I said perturbed.

"No. I was just trying to show you the lunacy of my mother. I think it all goes back to her. It's amazing I turned out as good as I did," he explained and he went back to making strange contorted faces. I wanted to laugh, but he was not trying to make me laugh. It was no joke!

"I suffered terrible psychological torment at her hands, that even after years of therapy I can't get over it. I think that's why I can't open my heart fully. I hate her."

"What did she do?" I gave myself permission to blatantly ask, since he was unloading a lifetime of problems and spilling out all issues at me in one blow.

"Well, she…she…It's hard to explain, the years of twisted psychological manipulation she used on me," he said starting to contract his body and wipe his arms as if bugs were attacking him and he was trying to shake them off. And then he went back to making the crazy-looking faces. I felt an urge to set him up with Pocahontas Dummkopf. I figured they would understand the meaning of each other's contorted facial lingo jive.

"Did she sexually molest you?" I asked.

"No, but kinda felt like it."

"Did she beat you or demean you all the time?"

"Well, no…but she just knew how to get into me and make me feel horrible."

I couldn't get one concrete way she had abused him except the faces and body language that spoke of being infested with bugs. After years of therapy you think he would have been able to understand it a bit better, but I guess he was still figuring it out.

I was in the full swing of my experience and when you've been touched by God the way I had, you tend to want to share it with the world. All I needed was my revival tent, my pulpit, and my white suit, because I was here to share the beauty of existence and awaken souls from their man-made, delusional pain into the heaven on earth, reconnecting everyone to their heart. I was in total love with my God experience. I was proselytizing to Lazy Boy and he was eating it up in-between his contorted facial conniption fits.

Lazy Boy was intrigued. Apparently, he did yoga, and followed different spiritual teachers, but the deeper experience he craved not only eluded him, but he was a miserable, sad, embittered person.

Although there wasn't a sexual attraction, there was an energy pull, so I was open to at least being friendly and seeing what might present itself through this sad, grinchy man. That's a book for you: "The Grinch That Wanted Sacred Sex with Cindy Lou Who." Lazy Boy needed his heart to grow three times the size, too, just like the Grinch.

On my occasional visits with Lazy Boy I would pass on what I was learning from Thad and he always seemed so intrigued, but being true to his nickname he didn't budge to go see Thad or any of the women who trained under Thad to become practitioners. Lazy Boy, like many men, was leery of having a man do bodywork on him. He kept saying he preferred if I taught him. He had already learned other kinds of meditation and did yoga, but he just seemed stuck in some whining place of not being able to "experience" the joys, release and calm that others on these spiritual paths seemed to be experiencing around him.

Lazy Boy was obviously developing a crush on me and I surprisingly found his energy suddenly playing on my sexual strings. The clown was not so funny in private. I couldn't believe he was this great comedian, so I had to watch some of his old television shows to see just how talented he was. His shows were good. He had reached the success he had sought and yet there was the pitiful sad cliché clown before me.

Lazy Boy and I finally kissed in one of our visits and I don't have words for it, not because it was so great, but because it was so unmemorable, I don't recollect. Well, the tantric experience was not at hand, just yet. I do remember he was not overly pushy as some men are to go further, which was a relief. He mentioned being worried about diseases. So the day he touched my boot must have been a real sign of submissiveness.

Up until this point, I had only experienced great bliss, new joy, and at-home-pleasure in my body. But a new feeling sprung up out of nowhere. I started to feel a tension and tightness in my throat that I had no explanation for. It would come and go. Now in this new re-sensitized state everything was magnified. This tightness was intense and it let it be known that there were emotions to it, that were like feeble, hazy apparitions that you could get a glimpse of through the corner of your eye, but could not concretely be identified. It was just a strange lump in the throat that made it hard to speak. I knew enough to know this was part of the spiritual unfolding taking place. It was part of the process of things coming out of my subconscious somatically. My body was speaking to me in its own language, one that I had to relearn.

It made me realize just how badly Lazy Boy needed this work to crack him into his subconscious. He obviously had so much torturing him somatically with all those contorted faces and contracted, invisible bug battles. He postured with his body over the trauma from his mother that he couldn't put into words.

Lazy Boy was not showing the signs of the sensual tantric potential, yet through our casual friendship a bond started to grow. I guess I wanted to help this sorrowful man with his noble cause of opening his heart.

A frustration grew in me because I felt I could not reach him emotionally and that I could not help him feel the spiritual love for life in his heart. He seemed to believe what I said, so why didn't he just try Thad out, once?

The relationship with this friend remained in an awkward, static place, where he seemed to want to experience what I had, but took none of my suggestions as to how to seek it.

The tightness in my throat--as if I would not be able to speak--was growing over the days. I would meditate and the Life Force Energy would swirl around me and take me into a deep state, but then the throat tightness would appear again. I would pine to get closer to Lazy Boy to help him "see in his heart," but he could not connect.

One day the frustration with Lazy Boy sprung up in meditation. I sat and watched my state of mind swing back and forth from my "Small Self" perspective to my "Larger Self" perspective in regards to how I felt and understood, and how I wanted to react to Lazy Boy.

"Small Self" was becoming upset and impatient with Lazy Boy and I started to feel that maybe he didn't deserve my caring. On the one hand he seemed very reluctant to try practicing what I suggested, and on the other, he was anxious to hear about it all the time. And after all, what was I getting? I certainly was not being showered with love or fun. I just got a lot of whining and complaining about life and his neurosis.

My "Larger Self" loved him unconditionally and had the space, vastness, and fullness to not care if "I" got anything out of it. I already had so much; I had extra to give. It was this amazing healing love that could not turn away from those in need. I literally sat and watched my perception swing back and forth between these two different extreme viewpoints of my being. I suppose we have this inner conflict going on all the time in small ways, but aren't hyperaware of it. Everything was being shown to me in an exaggerated way so that I really could see my inner workings.

Then the mysterious throat tension started gripping me to the point of producing a pain in my heart. I radically craved to be in nature, so I went hiking to relieve the tension.

The moment I stepped on the trail it was as if the forest fairies lifted a veil of angst from me and again I was in profound communion with everything. The colors, the smells, the gratitude came to the forefront of my experience. Nature is a great healer for me. And the "Larger Self" won out for the rest of the day.

When I began to climb up the trail my sped-up thoughts and messages from nature were implanting in my head. As I scrambled up one particular vertical stretch of the path on all fours, the earth came into my being and I understood her as the most perfect mother. Her love was so luscious and full, I began to cry. I felt so cared for, so protected, and safe. If only Lazy Boy could connect to the Universal Mother energy through nature he would receive the love imprint, the protective loving mother imprint he had not received by his biological mother. If only he could tap into this energy, he may finally be capable of trusting life deeply enough to lay his heart fully open. If only…

At every turn of this new path lessons were coming at me from every corner of life. The teacher in me had awakened to see and feel the lessons everywhere. The lessons in nature are especially vivid and clear in conveying their wisdom.

I would remain open to seeing if I could help him connect to this understanding. I would not kick him to the curb as I would've done in my "Small Self" of the past to someone so self-absorbed and who didn't really have much to offer to me, except his pain and longing for love, and some weak excuse for making out a little.

This was the beginning of a new struggle and conflict with redefining my boundaries in the world. Was I to live from my "Small Self" or my "Large Self" or would I have to integrate them both in a new way that would not shut down my heart? There seemed to be a chaotic phase of redefining life and boundaries as the old self was being deconstructed and the new self was emerging.

Lazy Boy cancelled a date with me at the last minute. I felt a severing of connection that was not verbal, but intuitive. As I felt the communication wane, I felt the tension in the throat start to constrict my chest. The epicenter would jolt my heart with pain and radiate down my arms. It was so painful I wondered why it didn't kill me. I literally felt like I was being crucified. I could not connect this pain to Lazy Boy's lack of romantic attention, because I was not interested in him in that way. I never felt inspired to have sex with him.

Was I feeling his pain? Was it a sense of my inability to connect to him or failure thereof? Or had some part of our interaction triggered the intensity of the already budding throat pain. Perhaps it had nothing to do with him at all. It was not clear, yet, what all this pain was about. I just knew it was part of the kundalini continuing to rub my nose in my energy blocks and it felt like it was killing me!

Day in and day out I felt the cross of pain on my chest. I just would meditate as much as possible. When I'm in pain I have developed the habit of just sitting in meditation, hiking, working out, and talking to friends. I've been so blessed to never have opened myself to any self-soothing negative habits in dealing with pain, like drugs, sex, shopping, or food addictions, so basically there are no thoughts or desires to do anything but sit with the pain through a normal day's routine. This is one of the things that I am most thankful to have attained through my meditation practice.

This time the pain that was crucifying me was so much more intense than anything I had felt ever. I kept wondering how I could feel so much physical pain in my heart and not have a heart attack! It was exhausting to walk around with this emotional pain; but the sun would come up and the sun would go down and I had to endure it.

I had been reading a book that came highly recommended by Thad, "A Path with Heart" by Jack Kornfield. It is a grounded, beautiful, intelligent sharing of great wisdom and insight into a healthy spiritual path. The truth written by an inspired voice on the path is always comforting to help us remember we are on the journey toward seeking deeper love together. The book became a significant catalyst for me in this episode of uncovering blocks as the inner teacher uses whatever it has at hand.

One day sitting with the crucifying pain in a morning meditation, the simplest sentence from "A Path with Heart" went beyond inspiration. It came to vibrate as truth in my being, literally! The statement "A true open heart doesn't close, no matter what, even when experiencing great pain" popped in my head. I had read it the night before with not a bit of feeling attached to it, except for the thought of how pleasantly idealistic it sounded. Could this phrase be simpler?

Suddenly, this thought came alive in the subconscious dimension I was now able to access. The thought was like a pinball, no, a wrecking ball that shot through my being. I felt and saw my body as a matrix of energy with different geometric patterns made of thought, held in my subconscious. And this subconscious field of patterned energy-thought was strewn out and held throughout my body as tension.

I saw my heart and it had its edges slightly crinkled and folded in. I saw that the sadness of life's disappointment in not being able to connect at a deeper heart level with my father and others throughout life, feeling they couldn't see me for who I really was.

The wrecking ball of the new thought shot through my energy matrix pinging and spinning, breaking-up the different energy/thought patterns that created the pain in my heart. My being was lighting up as the new thought whirled its way through me, spinning the energy matrix to settle into a new thought pattern that embodied the truth of that simple statement: "A true open heart stays open, no matter what. Even when experiencing great pain."

Small, subtle events, nothing traumatic, had built up and I had not kept my heart completely open. How many times did I have to keep opening up my heart? Apparently, endlessly!

Little thoughts, lies that negate the ultimate truth, that claim that outward status and perfection are more important than heart and emotional honesty to feel complete and successful, planted throughout my life's experiences had crept in and distorted my perception in subtle ways that ended up coloring my whole life. The pinball thought flew with such speed that all these thoughts, visions, energy pattern changes and realizations happened in an instant!

So many years of holding these thought/energy blocks and now they were being released and rearranged at lightning speed! This was a miracle. Energy can move so fast. Thought is energy, and the key is to learn how to move energy. Thought/energy can be moved, rearranged instantaneously. This was a peek into the world of how miracles are possible. It's all about learning to move energy as thought and form and in some states of mind it is far easier, instantaneous, and in other states of mind it can take a lifetime. Thank you, Jack Kornfield! Thank you, Thad! Thank you, my Larger Self!

The crucifying pain was gone. I was a ribbon unraveling into a kite of flying bliss. I vowed never to close my heart again. The repercussions of closing the heart and avoiding confronting painful situations or memories is so much more damaging than feeling the pain and working through it. If you hide from pain you relive it in little ways all your life, all your days, through a warped lens of perception. It takes courage, but trust me, when you realize that the little bits of unconfronted pain in your being are preventing you from living fully, there is no choice. When you realize you don't want to be "crucified" by your mental thought patterns, you have no choice.

My body taught me a huge lesson. I was carrying around a pain that only in this hyper-sensitized and vulnerable state could I realize was layered in my being and affecting the way that I was running my life. Bring it on! More pain, more life, more mystery unraveling. I am ready. Bring it on! Just break me open! It's more than worth it. It's the mystery of who I am unfolding before me. And I say this from the vantage point that things were coming up and releasing so quickly that I wanted to keep freeing myself from blocks. Not that I like pain, but the work of confronting the pain was worth it. I say this from a place where bliss was always on the other side of the pain that was coming up.

"So, you decide to use life to free yourself. You become willing to pay any price for the freedom of your soul. You will realize that the only price you have to pay is letting go of yourself. Only you can take inner freedom away from yourself, or give it to yourself."

-Michael A. Singer
'The Untethered Soul"

I excitedly shared with Thad my new epiphanies. He seemed to be as amazed at how continuous my lessons were presenting themselves. Once again, I was rolling and contorting in bliss on his table and in full body orgasm. Life Force Energy was searing the truth in my consciousness, telling me that I was at home in my body as long as my heart was open and I was in communion with the Force in everything, especially my body temple.

I had some further friendly communication over the next few weeks with Lazy Boy as the friendship petered out. One of the last times we spoke he shared with me that there was some girl that he had been dating off and on who was back in his life and she wanted to get married, but he couldn't bring himself to commit. He wasn't sure that he could ever commit if he couldn't open his heart, but at least he did have a nice house to be miserable in.

Something happened to me that had never happened before and never happened again. I never was attracted to Lazy Boy enough to want to have sex with him. I could tell he would've been a miserable sacred sex partner, even though I had developed some odd crush on him. It's the oddest feeling to have, to feel like you have a romantic crush on someone, but not even really want to kiss that person. I realized I was in love with his desire to open his heart and to be so honest about it. But the experience was part of a greater lesson that was beginning to moil and would be my cross to bear in the seeking of a sacred sex partner. Was I drawn to partners or subjects to study the human psyche?

We all have several crosses to bear in life: A death that must be suffered for a new life to break through – a new level of living in the truth of God and the glory of our potential for a joyous life on earth. Each cross we must bear is a chance to drop a belief system that, if left in the unconscious, can fate our actions and lead us to live a life devoid of true love and ultimately ecstasy. Jesus did not die for our sins. No one can die for our sins. We must die for our sinful ignorance. The part of us that does not live in truth and love and holds onto distorted belief systems must die.

It hurts to awaken to the belief systems that are ruining our life, that hold our happiness hostage. But sometimes at the height of pain the movement of change is most possible, and we can drop the burden of thought that crucifies us and the heart is released, sent soaring back into the comfort and the eternal love of spirit.

The friction of my ignorance was coming to life through the mysterious heart pain that invaded me, and I was longing, straining to see what it was, but most of all I was still, hanging with it, not trying to find distractions or escape. As it grew, I was preparing myself to jump into the chasm of the unknown, to be reborn. I saw in Lazy Boy what happens when you don't make a conscious decision to let your sins, your false belief systems die and I wasn't going to let that happen to me. But this is where it gets tricky. What is it that despite living in so much unhappiness kept Lazy Boy from letting his sinful ignorance die? I longed to learn more about how to help others; for what has opened me may not open another, for we are all at different stages of awareness and we are wired differently. Thad was starting a training course for the therapy he does and every time I entertained the idea of participating, I would feel butterflies of anticipation and possibility. I longed to know more.

* * *

Lazy Boy died as I wrote this book. I never heard from him or ran into him again after our last conversation about his girlfriend who wanted to get married but he was still perplexed as to how to open his heart like he longed to do.

9

"The Raw Meat-eating Dwarf and the Poisoned Apple"

I was driving, winding up the curvy roads in the mountain tops of deep Malibu to meet Doc, a nutritionist, who was supposed to be the next step in Thad's process of opening up to deeper levels of energy sensitivity. Finding addresses up in this rustic area of Malibu is not easy. The homes are far apart and isolated from one another. I wasn't even seeing people outside of their property to stop and ask for directions. After negotiating the sharp turns that led to the landmark he had mentioned, I decided the small, run-down wood cabin was my best bet. I drove down the dirt road leading up to the rickety outpost.

A stocky, short, barrel-chested bald man came running out to welcome me and waved me in. It was Doc!

"I was just making some lunch. Come in and join me." I walked into the cabin and there was some white creamy stuff coming out of a food press. "I'm making coconut cream, one of the most nutritious foods on the planet. I want to show you how to make a delicious shake that you'll be having everyday as part of your program." He added raw eggs, a banana, honey, and the coconut cream and blended it up as he started searing a filet mignon.

Doc certainly was not in a rush to squeeze me into a fifteen-minute time slot as most doctors do these days. Our appointment would last three hours! He made a wonderful lightly seared fillet mignon on salad. He lectured me on the nutritional wonders of coconut as he made a delicious shake.

Now, this is the way a healer and nutritionist should greet you, with a healthy meal that he shows you how to prepare. This ritual of feeding me before our appointments became a very nurturing practice throughout my treatment with Doc.

Looking into my eyes and assessing through his knowledge of iridology, Doc began his examination. He felt pulses as an acupuncturist would and hooked me onto a machine where he put different ampoules that would somehow read what my health problems were and what supplements would energetically balance my body.

"Lay on the table. I'm going to work on you," Doc ordered and I wasn't going to argue about getting some massage therapy. He worked on me just as Thad did, but went deeper and harder. I grimaced. "That hurts, huh?" he asked.

"Yes. Of course, but I can take it," I replied.

"One day when you are properly and completely detoxified when someone rubs you this hard you won't feel any pain, you'll just feel the breath and joy of God, the bliss, go through you."

"What are you talking about? With my lifestyle from dancing or flying off of horses I will always be tight and sore," I said. "Let's not get carried away with extreme statements or I'll think you're a nut case," I said jokingly. "You know the only reason I'm listening to everything you say and taking it to heart is because Thad recommended you. What Thad's work has done for me so far is so amazing that if he says something will help me awaken and become more aware of my energy body, I'm willing to try it, just short of shooting myself."

"Well, maybe every now and then you'll be achy from your athletic lifestyle, but most people don't know that so much pain in the flesh is caused by toxins. Thad himself could only go so far in how flexible his body could be in yoga until he started to do proper detox. Well, it's good you have a real motivation to try the program, because it's pretty radical. It's just short of shooting yourself."

"Lay it on me."

"It's an all-raw meat diet."

"RAW MEAT! Even lamb?"

"Even lamb."

"Chicken, too?"

"Even raw chicken," he said and I swallowed hard anticipating the disgusting factor.

This diet included raw: eggs, dairy, chicken, fish, lamb, beef, cheese, and lots of coconut cream. I never would've dreamt this one up. And very few vegetables and grains!

When I was younger I was vegetarian for a few years until in a deep group meditation, the mind empty, the body floating to where I couldn't feel it…a vision popped into my head…a steaming pepper steak floating in front of me and for the first time in two years I craved meat!

I felt it was a message from my soul and I got up to go get me some meat! On my way out of the meditation a few of the "higher-ups" stopped me.

"Where are you going? We aren't finished with the meditation program," a busy body named Sarah asked.

"Well, I had a vision of a pepper steak and now I feel like I've got to get some!" I answered.

Sarah and her friend Clare, another busy body, were mouth-open shocked. They looked at each other fumbling for words.

"You eat meat?" Clare asked in a patronizing tone.

"No, But I'm about to." I answered.

"We're not supposed to eat meat for our spiritual growth. Very low vibration," Sarah said in an authoritarian manner laying down the law.

"Think about it. It has to be a temptation…ah, ah…you're being tempted by…by…" Clare reached for a convincing argument to counter the message delivered to me through the vision of a floating steak.

"…like the dark side…the devil!" Sarah chimed in looking at me as if I may be possessed. I just laughed.

"I thought the devil tempted people with drugs and greed, but he tempts me with meat? What am I, a dog?" I chuckled. "The message came from a deep peace. I felt it was a positive message. I felt the meaning strongly, clearly and it was my higher-self telling me to eat meat!"

"Ah…you should stay and sit with it and ah…see if you change your mind. Talk to the Guru about it."

"I'm hungry. I'm going to find me a steak," I said and they looked at me as if I had not only lost my mind, but couldn't believe I wasn't obeying their veteran advice.

I left the meditation and from that day forward started eating meat again.

Funny, a few months after that pepper stake vision I went to a nutritionist who was vegetarian herself, but she told me that I needed to eat meat to regenerate my body from an illness I had. Well, what do you know, the inner guide that sent me the pepper steak vision knew what I needed. I just had to still myself long enough to listen to the intuitive wisdom. One thing the inner wisdom forgot to impart was that it should be Raw Meat!

Raw meat! Raw lamb and chicken! How the hell do I get accustomed to that? Well, Doc put in a convincing argument as to why raw meat.

Apparently, besides having more vitamins and "live enzymes" that help you digest the meat, raw meats are more alkaline, whereas cooked meats are more acidic. The latest "word" in the world of health is that you want to have an alkaline diet. Diseases like cancer flourish in acidic environment, but can't survive in an alkaline environment.

The raw meats and dairy that come from grass-fed, organic, free-range animals have more omega-3 oils, like fish, unlike the corn-fed meats that are mostly saturated fats. Everyone knows that the omega-3 oils are the prized oils for health. So, eating organic, grass-fed animals is like eating fish. Also, the raw cream and raw animal fat is supposed to detoxify the body from harmful heavy metals such as mercury.

Okay, there seemed to be some sense to this raw meat and dairy rationale. I was warned that I could experience severe detoxification symptoms at the beginning, especially since Doc was also starting me out with a liver/gallbladder cleanse.

I went to a raw food market and stocked up on cheeses, cream, and butter from Amish farms, raw coconut cream, coconut water, and all the raw meats. I went home that night and braved into the most radical diet I ever dreamt of. My taste buds were downright rebellious. I felt like I was on one of those shows that makes you eat something so foreign and disgusting, like monkey anus, that even the at-home viewer is gagging; only I didn't have the carrot dangling in front of me of some large amount of prize money for incentive. But I did have the objective of widening the energy channels of the God orgasm experience as my bait.

I started with the liver/gallbladder cleanse. Thad says that with all the toxins in the environment it is recommended to do two cleanses a year.

The first few days into the raw diet the electricity went out completely in the neighborhood for the whole day. I remember sitting down to my first meal of raw lamb chops and thinking: "Hell, who needs electricity when you eat raw! I didn't have to cook anything." I almost gagged that first time. Raw lamb was the toughest at first. Like an idiot, I made it worse for myself as I didn't spice it up or put a sauce or make a tartar out of it. I just cut into it plain. But actually, over the first few weeks, I got used to the flavor and started to crave it. Odd, huh? The key is to learn to make tasty tartars.

The first two weeks I was absolutely exhausted from this new diet. I was sleeping ten hours a day and taking naps. I was groggy, drugged, hazy, and heavy, as if my body was made of slow-drying cement. Then my menstrual cycle came with a force I had not experienced! I was wiped out physically, in cramping pain and emotionally, totally flat. The herbs and the diet were proving to be a heavy-handed detoxifying challenge. Something was definitely happening. Maybe I was dying!

Suddenly, after two weeks my energy shifted and I seemed to have more energy than ever. I never had premenstrual symptoms or period difficulties again, as long as I ate mostly raw meat. I used to be able to tell when my period was coming due to the emotional shifts and tiredness, but if that happened to me now, it would surprise me since I no longer experience fluctuations…no PMS!

Before the raw diet I had started to wake up too early at times and I was often not able to fall back asleep to get a good night's rest. Since the kundalini awakening, oftentimes I'd be awakened by pangs of hunger at four or five in the morning, which compounded the lack of sleep issue. I would eat and still have trouble going back to sleep.

Once I was on the raw diet, I would wake up and make a raw egg, raw cream, raw honey, and banana shake and it would put me right back to sleep. The burning of the released kundalini energy seemed to speed up my metabolism. There is a lot of heat that seems to run through the body at times with the kundalini energy and I believe it literally burns calories. I also sensed there was some kind of regenerative process going on and my body needed those extra meals to heal. This is all just my theory on this odd feeling of starvation that would wake me up before dawn. I don't know exactly why this was happening, but now it comes and goes ever since my kundalini opening. My need for a greater amount of nourishment is connected to the amount of kundalini flowing, burning in me.

There's a story of a huge proponent of raw-foods, Ajonis Vanderplantz. Who could have made up a better name for one of the fathers of the raw meat diet? He said he was at one time out in the dessert and an old Indian man came to him and told him that the reason why the Indians of bygone days, from different indigenous tribes around the world, could maintain their vitality and health while living in harsh conditions, exposed to the elements all the time, was because they ate fresh meat and organ meats right after the kill. The Eskimo ate a lot of animal meats high in fats: raw seal meat and whale, which is very high in saturated and omega-3 fat, right after a kill and they too were a very hardy people with no heart problems. Ajonis claims that he cured himself of cancer and serious physical injury from a car accident on what he touts as a regenerative raw meat diet.

There is also a raw diet based on the findings of a Cleveland dentist Weston A. Price in the 1920's and 1930's. Over a period of ten years, Price discovered that his adult patients with severe dental problems also had other problems throughout their body such as arthritis, osteoporosis, diabetes, intestinal problems and chronic fatigue, asthma, allergies.

Price set out on a global trek to examine how other primitive societies' diets relate to health and dental problems. He found that those in other cultures had diets that were at least four times higher in minerals and vitamin C and B complex than the diets of Americans. Many of the healthy groups of people that Price studied ate special foods like cod liver oil, fish, eggs, organ meats, cream, butter, and raw unpasteurized whole milk from grass-fed cows. Price advocated eating what he calls nutrient-dense, natural and unprocessed foods. So there seems to be some interesting testimonial and rationale to support this odd, primitive raw-meat diet approach.

My conscious dialogue with the Life Force Energy continued to grow and I felt that the new diet was fueling my awakening even further! I felt like I was in a constant state of death and rebirth. My heart would break open yet again and I would realize there was an even deeper understanding to what it is to feel "alive."

Although the crucifying heart pain was gone, the tightness in the throat would still show up at times. It was a sign to me that I still was not aware of some emotional memory that I had to confront and that I needed to realize just exactly how it was affecting me. I kept feeling like something was stuck in my throat.

Then one day I walked into the house after a meditation of great union with nature and I grabbed my throat as a voice said to me that something was stuck and I needed to spit it up. As I turned the corner to walk down the hallway I had a vision that a piece of apple was stuck in my throat. "How funny is that," I thought to myself. "Why an apple?" I hadn't eaten an apple that day.

As I walked down the hall, the hall turned into a ghostly hologram of the black forest from the Snow While fairytale Disney movies! No joke! A *bona fide* open-eyed vision! There were dark, charred-looking trees, the branches of which looked like claws ready to come to life and grab me. The Wicked Witch was there holding out the apple on one side of the hallway and a few frightened dwarfs where hanging out in the tree roots, on the other side of the hallway. What the hell was happening!?

This awakening had opened a portal into my subconscious where my "Larger Self" could send messages to me in the language of the Gods: symbolic visions, dreams, and wakeful dreaming. At that instant, I remembered something that I had completely forgotten since I was a child, until this moment of wakeful dreaming.

When I was six years old I had a recurrent nightmare that the Wicked Witch from the "Snow White" tale was coming to my house to make me eat "the poisoned apple." In the dream I went into the kitchen and my whole family was there in our happy, warm household. Under the golden glow of the light my grandmother was at her sewing machine at the kitchen table telling stories with great gestures, as she was an animated storyteller. My mother was laughing by the stove, and the maid hustled around preparing dishes. My father and grandfather were there, enjoying each other's company too. There was goodness and I felt safe, but then I realized no one could see me!

I started screaming at them, warning them of the danger approaching, but they could not hear me either. And in absolute terror I watched through the kitchen window as the Wicked Witch came up the walkway with her basket of apples. I squatted down below the windowsill so that she wouldn't see me. I heard the door open. The witch was in the house and I knew I was doomed! No one could see me or hear me and therefore could not protect me.

Now I was living this nightmare **awake**! I was picking up at the point in the dream that would be logical and sequential, where I had I eaten the poisoned apple when I was six and had fallen into a deep-unconscious state resembling death, as had befallen Snow White. And now, I was kissed by my prince, the kundalini, the Life Force Energy, God itself, and I was coming out of my coma back to life! I was reclaiming parts of myself that had gone comatose when I swallowed a poisonous belief system at six years old, symbolized by the poisoned apple!

I was viscerally experiencing the point in the fairytale that symbolized Snow White's salvation, her resurrection. My struggle with this Poisoned Belief System had come full circle. I had swallowed the "Poisoned Apple" when I was six years old and now it was time for me to spit it up.

When I was six-years-old my Higher Self had tried to warn me that a part of me was dying or being put to sleep, but I was not mature enough to fight the belief systems that surrounded me.

And you thought magic wasn't real and fairytales were just for children! What intelligence is running the show that it picked something that my mind as a child could symbolically understand to try and warn me of what was about to befall me and then years later come back, pushing from the boggy marshes of the subconscious with such fanfare, in a wakeful dream in my hallway, to convey to me exactly what was happening to me. The channels were opening again and the dialogue with the mystical inner guide was coming back to life!

I realized through this experience that the "Higher Self" communicates through the "Higher Aspect" of the imagination with symbolic waking visions and dreams. And now that my channels to my inner-self were opening again, I didn't need to be asleep to receive these wisdom stories from my inner-guide. I could receive the language of the inner soul in a wakeful state.

Imagination has many purposes and the highest is allowing it to be used by your own "Higher Self" soul, to speak to you in the language of symbols that are threaded together to create metaphors and fairytales that tell stories of truth and guide us in our journey. In the same way, sex has many uses and levels of expression such as procreation, stress release, sucking energy out of another, love, and as a catalyst into the subconscious for healing physically and emotionally. And the highest aspect of sex is God Union, sacred sex!

The imagination has varying higher and lower degrees of purpose. And the highest is to dialogue with Spirit that, again, achieves God Union: tantra.

The Spirit most often takes things that are a point of reference to us from our brain files of life experience. Sometimes it will give us imagery, symbols from cultures or experiences that we have not known in this lifetime and we may have to research the symbology. And that is a most amazing testament to the highly intelligent collective unconscious that connects us all. How amazing that our "Whole Mind-Being" is working on so many layers that we are not usually aware of.

It felt so magical, because it is not how I was accustomed to functioning. But I believe it is how we are supposed to function if we wish to function optimally, wholly. We have different aspects of what constitutes being a human being and unfortunately, we have been taught to compartmentalize these aspects of ourselves and actually shut some down completely.

Our society has not just bred people, but institutions: medical, government branches, businesses, to specialize and compartmentalize. Slowly, the wisdom of how intricately things are related and work as a whole must be considered in order to progress both in the outer and inner worlds.

In regards to healing, medicine has become so specialized, that it has turned myopic and thus doctors often overlook many important aspects that contribute to healing and they tend to see a person as having an isolated broken part instead of as a whole being that needs to be treated with a more integrative approach to mind, body, and Spirit.

Can you imagine if I went to a medical doctor for the tightness in my throat? He would have prescribed muscle relaxants, or physical therapy, God knows what! But would he be able to open me to my subconscious to see what the body wisdom was trying to convey?

I've recently discovered that there are many therapeutic methods of breaking into the subconscious, but no mainstream doctor seemed to ever offer me this skill or ability. It was Thad's innate ability and his "Rule of Four" process that was helping me integrate the different parts of my being. I was blown away by the intelligence of my whole being working in concert. This is true magic, practical magic!

So, what was this poisoned belief system?

I never had any physical or mental abuse from my parents. I was only spanked twice in my entire life. Once I called my mother a bitch and she slapped me, deservedly so. The other time my father spanked me for throwing a matchbox car clear across the room at my older brother and nailing him in the tooth, knocking it loose. If you knew my brother as a kid he deserved to have a few more teeth knocked loose along the way, so I didn't deserve that spanking, but that's up for debate. So, how could I have shut down?

In my case it was a combination of programming my mind with societal norms and my father's belief about what it is to be successful. Kids are very intuitive and although I was never berated or punished relative to any belief system, I was earning approval and rewarded around certain belief systems.

My father's "God" and that of Western Civilization is the glorification of the attributes of the mind and intellect that are held above and apart from the rest of the person's being. These attributes are wonderful when led by the wisdom of the heart that comes through feeling and the higher aspect of intuition.

But I picked up from my father that emotions were a waste of time and that a need for believing in God or a higher universal creative intelligence beyond the intellect was a weakness. My father hated the hypocrisy of the clergy in all religions and the wars incited by religious differences. He also shut down his emotions from childhood trauma and threw himself into excelling and became a type "A" successful juggernaut.

Unfortunately, he was not aware enough to know that there is a difference between being religious and Spiritually intuitive. The message I received was to cut off from my very strong spiritual intuitive nature. He never dealt with his deeper emotional issues and certainly didn't want to deal with mine, so he was teaching me it was best to try and ignore my emotional self. And now that I look back and connect the dots I realize my greatest gifts came from this ability to connect to heart/Spirit/God. I was being taught that the best parts of me were to be suppressed.

At the age of nine the poisoned belief system grew enough to make me feel that I was not understood. I felt that people couldn't see the real me. There was a sense of isolation and disconnection because I had been trained to cut off from a whole side of myself. So then, I fell into wanting to please those around me unnecessarily so that I would "be seen" in their terms and fell into anorexic behavior, because that's what it would take to be the best in ballet and be successful, just like my father was the best.

I wanted to be special, as we all do. But in reality, we can't be special unless we feel that we are so through our connection to our heart.

There is no bitterness or blame. I feel so grateful and blessed to have the parents I have. I know my father loved me very much and his inability to deal with emotions came from his own wounding.

When he became aware of the damage he was doing he reached out emotionally and became my greatest supporter in my spiritual path. When I wanted to see the Dalai Lama he drove me to his event, even though he found it boring and slept through it. When we traveled together and I wished to seek out shamans he would make time in the itinerary and take pictures even if he didn't participate or believe in them.

Although my father stepped up and remolded an emotional relationship with me, in the deepest place of my subconscious I was still operating from this harmful belief system. Just because I understood things intellectually, it did not mean that my subconscious, my energy matrix, had released it, re-patterned the thought process.

Now, I could see how deep and reality-altering this process could be. And although my trauma was nothing compared to traumas experienced by other less fortunate human beings, it still took much courage to deal with it. I have so much respect and admiration for those who have to tackle bigger traumas. But it is worth working on it if you want to be fully alive. One has to let go of the walls and the baggage. It is the journey of the inner warrior. It takes great courage!

And as my journey to reclaim and reconnect to the sacred in all of my life continued, I realized it was time to listen to the Life Force Energy and seek out my tantric sex lover. The Life Force was guiding me to feel new love, new bliss, and I was going to listen. I was ready to take real action! I would get up the courage to call my friend "The Guru Agent." Perhaps he could be my tantric sex matchmaker!!!

10

"Back at the Gym"

It was the usual parade of "hellos" and nods of greeting as I walked through the gym and up the stairs. As I ascended the steps and stepped onto the weight room floor I waved to my Colombian friend Marita. Once she registered it was me, she waved me over frantically. "I made haste," as Shakespeare oft says in his plays.

"Suraya, Surayita! Come, come. Quick!" she urged conspiratorially. "Remember I spoke to you about that guy that I wanted to set you up with that I couldn't remember his name? We'll it's Mancho," she said giddily and giggling at her poor memory. "Well, he's right down there by the café," she said pointing down the stairwell at a muscular, tanned, dark haired man.

"Oh, him? Yeah, I've seen him around," I said not too excited.

"What do you think? He's cute, yes? I already spoke to him about you and he says he's interested and wants to take you out. He knows who you are," she said pleased with herself, with the idea of making a match for two of her supposedly favorite singles at the gym. With these overly gushing, sweet Latinas that tell everyone they are their favorite person you never know if you truly are their favorite.

"He's cute, but ah, no, not interested," I replied without hesitation.

"Why not? He's so handsome," she complained.

"He's a player and too superficial. Not interested in that type," I said.

"Oh, my God! You're right! How can you tell?"

"I can tell in an instant by looking at the way he moves and postures his body. Oh, and the way I've seen him look in the mirror. First, he is too self-conscious about how hot he is. Secondly, he just has that sleazy, hungry look of having to sleep with everybody for sport to validate that he is a desirable man. Someone like that has often grown up not feeling too attractive and needs constant approval," I explained. Marita put her hand over her mouth astounded and to contain her laughter.

"You're absolutely right. He is a Don Juan," she said with childlike amusement, surprised that I could see through him so easily.

"But why would you try to set me up with someone like him if you already knew all that?" I asked not so amused myself.

"Well, everyone has to mature and he says that he would like to find that woman that will make him want to change. Some men just have to find the right woman," she responded. "He's really a nice guy. Very funny too!"

"No, not interested. But thanks for thinking of me," I said.

"You have to come salsa dancing with me and my husband, again. You're such a good dancer. I loved watching you dance last time." She spread out the invitation so warmly with her cushiony, motherly Latina voice it had the comforting effect of a savory home- cooked meal. I felt nurtured.

"I'd love to! I've just been so busy. Soon though, soon," I assured.

"You always say that. Life is short! Make sure to fill it with fun!" she said as she spotted her husband Angus, a South African, blue-eyed red-head with a ruddy complexion. "Oh, look! He is *mi amor*! *Es tan bello*--so beautiful! I'm so lucky! He's my everything! He is so good to me! The best thing that ever happened to me! He raised my three boys. Their father was never there, but he stepped in and took care of us. *Corazon de oro*--heart of gold! I want you to find someone just as wonderful," she said as he came over to join us. "There you are mi *amorcito*! Love of my life!" she addressed him, showering him with love and grabbing his face and kissing him. "Look, he is so wonderful! He is the best man ever!" If anyone knew how to build her man up, she did. Every time I ran into them it was the same thing with the adoration and compliments that affirmed to the world that he was her hero.

"So, did you tell Suraya about Mancho?"

"Si, *mi amorcito,* but she no like him. Listen, you're not going to believe it, but she could tell he's a Don Juan, a player. Isn't that unbelievable? And you know she's right."

"Yeah, you're right. We're hopeful he may change, but it's not fair to put you in an experimental place when odds are that he's still a lout. I don't know what we were thinking," he said surprisingly. "But then again, you never know. He says he would like to change."

"Yeah, I'll pass," I said. "I don't have the energy for that kind of deal."

"Well, the wheels are set in motion so he may be approaching you. Let him down easily. Even men can be sensitive about rejection," he advised. Well, that setup ended with the matchmakers themselves retracting the match. Ha! "Come on Marita I'm starving. Let's go get some dinner." They started to walk away.

"Oh, yes *mi amorcito* –my love! Let's feed you *papacito bello*–my beautiful, beautiful baby. I have made you some special Colombian food for tonight that you love. Your favorite! I so want you to be happy."

"I love it! Let's go eat! Good seeing you Suraya. You have to come dancing with us soon!"

"Yes, for sure!" I nodded.

"*Adiós mi* Surayita!" she said as they descended the steps. Now, that's a happy couple for you! And they're always like that.

I went over to the jumping platforms when Buddy moseyed over with a couple of friends of his.

"Hey Suraya!"

"Hey guys!"

"I can't stand young girls. I like older women," he declared out of the blue, leaving his friends and me taken aback by this statement coming from a seventeen-year-old. I wondered if he wasn't flirting with me and trying to be suggestive. He seemed a little more upbeat when seeking me out to chat lately when I ran into him at the gym since he broke up with his girlfriend.

"Why would you say that?" I asked. "What is it about girls your own age you don't like?" I asked.

"Yeah, why is that dude?" his friend Jasper said, a thin, cut twenty-six-year-old who was new to the gym. Jasper's flawless white skin always impressed me. His dark eyebrows buoyantly bobbed up and down on his forehead like those of a classically expressive Italian.

"Young girls are like whores. They sleep with everyone and get diseases. Older girls are more selective and they aren't such and I don't like to have to wear a condom," he said out loud in the gym for all to hear. I guess he got used to our open discussions about sex at the gym and didn't feel he had to hide anything. His friends and I roared with laughter.

"Ok dude, get this straight. You got it all wrong. You should like it that they are sluts and you should wear a fucking condom. What are you, an idiot? You should always wear a condom. What are you thinking?" Eon, his other friend said, trying to set him right. Eon, a classic square-jawed, California-good-looking, effortlessly fit jock was about twenty-eight years. Most of Buddy's friends were much older, interestingly enough. Buddy was homeschooled, but had no problem making friends and seemed to be drawn to older people in general. We all continued to laugh at the absurdity of Buddy's deduction regarding the difference between older vs. younger women.

"Well, I still prefer older women. They're more interesting. The girls I like are a lot older," he countered, sticking to his guns.

"Who do you like?" I asked. "It sounds like you have had some experience in the matter."

"Yeah, who are these women?" Jasper said and knocked Buddy with his shoulder playfully.

"Well, I have a crush on that thirty-year-old law student, Melissa, with those big lips. She's so hot!" I instantly knew who he was talking about, but was surprised as I thought she looked anorexic. I actually felt bad for her, because there was something very unhealthy going on with her. Well, at least it wasn't me. "We were talking a lot and she's really cool," he continued. "She even is into professional football. We were going to hang out and then when I told her how old I am, she didn't want to hang with me anymore. That's my problem. When I like someone and they find out my age," he said stymied.

"Good! You need to quit that," Eon said shaking his head.

"You'll be fine. I do recommend you stick to girls closer to your own age. You're still jailbait for Melissa," I added.

"Yeah, that's what we tell him, but he doesn't listen," Jasper summed it up.

"Ok, well, always a good laugh with you guys. Got to get to my workout," I said as I walked away. Then Buddy called after me.

"Hey, I asked my dad about lending you the chainsaw and he wanted to meet you to make sure you know how to use it."

"Yeah, I've used one before. I can meet him anytime," I replied.

"The only problem is that he went out of town for a couple of weeks."

"Well, if I can't find one sooner I'll tap you again," I said as I continued walking on. "Thanks for asking."

As I passed one of the familiar faces I've seen at the gym over the years, my little intuitive voice that was growing told me that he had a chainsaw. I thought to myself that I might as well ask, now that the universe put it in my head. So, without hesitation, I went over to this grey-haired older gentleman to find out.

"Hello. My name is Suraya."

"Hi Suraya. Brett," he said smiling and open to my unsuspected approach.

"I was wondering if you have a chainsaw," I asked. His eyes opened wide with amusement and surprise as he chuckled.

"Why do you think I would have a chainsaw? Do I look like a serial killer or something?" he asked, entertained by this out-of-left-field inquiry.

"No. I don't think you look like a killer," I laughed. "I just had a feeling that you have a chainsaw. I can't explain it. Call it intuition. I'm looking for a chainsaw to cut some trees for my mother. I don't want to have to rent one at Home Depot. It's so far."

"I see," he said laughing even harder. "Well, yes I do have a chainsaw."

"Can I borrow it for a day?" I asked.

"Really? You? You're going to cut the trees, yourself? That's so nice of you."

"I've seen you here for years. You can trust me," I assured.

"I'm not worried you're going to steal it for crying out loud." He continued to laugh. "I'll lend it to you if you know how to use one. I don't want you getting hurt."

"Actually, I've used one before. I don't know what the big deal is." I nodded pleased with myself.

"Oh, nice! I'm surprised. What have you used it for in the past?"

"One of my first boyfriends was in architecture school and his best friend's brother got married super young and his wife got pregnant," I began.

"What? Your who? Your boyfriend's friend's brother?"

"Yes."

"This is going to be a long story," he laughed as he continued to lift the stack of weights while he listened.

"Well, they were poor, organic farmers in San Diego, so his brother designed a straw bale house, which is super cheap to build, for the young family. The insulation of the straw keeps the house super cool in summer and keeps the heat in during winter. His brother then got his friends from the architecture school and a few of their old friends from back in San Diego together for a good-old-fashioned house-raising party," I explained.

"Nice, nice!" A wholesome, Hallmark-card smile spread across his face.

"So, my boyfriend asked me and my best friend to come and help. He said the women could cook the meals while the men built the house. I told him that if I was going to go down to help out, I wanted it to be a new experience and that I, and my best friend at the time, would want to help build the house, not cook."

"Oh, wow! Impressive."

"Yes, it was a story to remember on many levels. You don't know the drama."

"I'm sure you'll tell me. Go on."

"So, we head out to the farm and we're in a rush and we're a bit late and we're speeding down, weaving between cars. Then suddenly I started to hear a weird thunk-like noise as if something was wrong with the tire. I told my boyfriend to exit the freeway to check it out. He tried to persuade me it was nothing to worry about and that we were in a rush, but the strange noise persisted. I insisted he exit immediately.

Just as he finally agreed, there was a serious banging in the engine, smoke started to come out of the hood, then we lost power. We managed to coast off the exit and call AAA. They came and gave us the shocking news that there had been a leak in the coolant and we had melted the engine of my car completely!!

So strange how you take things so differently when you're young. I didn't miss a beat, I didn't cry. I just accepted it and let it go. I would be so devastated now if I did that to my car. We just rented a car and were on our way.

After a night of laughter and dancing around the hay, we rose soon after the crack of dawn on the farm and I in my Daisy Duke cutoff shorts was ready for the house raising!

When building a straw-bale house you start by cutting the bale of straw. So, we hauled the bales in place, stacking them up to make the walls of the house, and that is where we had to use the chainsaw. We had to cut some of the blocks of hay to fit the sizes needed for the configuration. So, once we built the hay up to a certain height, we had to hammer in the rib bar to hold the bale into place.

After hammering rib bars most of the day I wanted to try something new, so I asked to have a crack at cutting the bales of hay with the chainsaw. Everyone made such a big deal about it and gave me so much advice. Lord, I thought it was going to be so difficult!

Then it was my moment. I walked toward the chainsaw. Everyone stopped working, stopped talking and stared at me, even all the boys atop the bale wall looked down at me. My girlfriend stopped and watched me with a whimsical smile as we always joined each other on new adventures and she was excited for me to try yet another new challenge. It was a little nerve-wracking since all eyes were on me, but I steered the course and picked up the chainsaw. I started the chainsaw and then sliced into the bale...and it was easy as pie! Everyone broke out into cheers and clapped. I couldn't believe it was so easy after all the warnings they gave me. My bestie and I proved to be just as capable as the men. They were impressed. Needless to say, it was one torturously hot day and we cooked ourselves into a good tan and were exhausted from working all day in the blazing sun.

Thus, I learned to use a chainsaw, but I wrecked my car. It was unsalvageable."

"Wow! I feel transported from that story. I left the gym and I was there with hay in my hair, a light sunburn and the sound of hammering rib bar and a chainsaw. In fact, I'm not a hundred percent back, yet," he said making me chuckle. "That was great! You can come by and get the chainsaw anytime and pick out any other tools you may like. I have every tool you can think of. I'm in the process of finishing building my house." He started to laugh like a slow starting car and I joined in his laughter once it got going.

The humorous coincidence that I happened to ask someone who was building his own house himself and had every tool including a chainsaw did not elude us: A little spooky. Was it my growing psychic intuition or pure coincidence?

"Hey, how about him?" he pointed randomly to a man at a weight machine that neither one of us knew. "Does he have a chainsaw?" he asked, testing this so-called *feeling* I claimed to have.

"No. He doesn't, but that guy next to him does." I pointed to the men and spoke loudly so that they knew I was speaking to them. The men seemed bemused and confused.

"Nope. Don't have a chainsaw," one said. "Why?"

"Just a little psychic poll," I explained to the man. It obviously made no sense to the man and he laughed and continued his workout.

"Yes. I do have a chainsaw. But it needs to be repaired," the other man answered.

"Ah, ha, ha, ha!" Brett laughed heartily. "OK, Ok. The girl has a little bit of that funny Ouija-board energy to her. Take my number and call me when you want to come and pick it up. I live up Topanga," he concluded.

"Thanks, I'll give you a holler. Bye Brett!"

* * *

On my way out my friend Mark, a thirty-six-year-old, tanned, thin but muscled bleached-blond surfer type, that more and more walked and dressed like a cool-cat pimp and player straight out of the seventies, headed me off at the steps. I paused to listen to what he had to say.

"Surayray! You lookin' so beautiful as usual. How is it that you never age? What do you do? What do you eat?"

"Aw! You're so sweet!" I said.

"Hey, just so you know, that kid, Buddy, was telling his friends in the locker room the other day that he is going to *smash* or *smoosh* you.

"How funny! Just like they say on 'The Jersey Shore'," I said.

"One of those new words for fuck. What kind of word is 'I'm going to *smoosh* her? It's so, sooo weak. In my days we were real hombres. I would say I'm going to destroy that!" he joked.

"Oh, yeah, that sounds so much better," I said facetiously and we laughed. "*Smoosh* is kinda cozy, like squishing a marshmallow."

"Now that you put it that way, I think you look very 'squishable,' he said joking, as the eternal jester that he is. Just so you know, he was talking as if it was a done deal. He had it all wrapped up with you. So, you were right, he has a sex crush on you if that's what you call it when someone wants to squish you like a marshmallow. I like to melt my marshmallows in hot chocolate. You wanna come check out my new Jacuzzi and be my melting marshmallow? I'm sure my girlfriend won't mind. I'll just say you're my marshmallow friend, Suraya," he said and laughed like the playful, silly children we are together. We have that friendship of the *eternal child* where everything is funny and everything that is said is silly. He was not hitting on me. It was just our silly childish banter.

"So funny, Buddy keeps beating around the bush talking about how he's into older women and using other girls as examples. I'm sure he really likes the other women too. He's a kid looking for experience. Wanting to sleep with everyone. Thanks for letting me know." I said.

"Oh, and he said you were coming after him! Can you beat that!"

"Ha! That's funny. Wouldn't touch the kid with a ten-foot pole. I guess no more sharing romantic sex stories to broaden his horizons. Boys and men are so funny how they brag. I've had a couple of people in here say that they have slept with me. One I never touched and the other one I only kissed. I set them both straight."

"Well, just thought you should know what's out there in the locker-room talk," Mark said. "Got to go. See ya!"

"Thanks Marky Mark! My hot chocolate and marshmallow lover."

I went up to the gym café counter to order a smoothie and some berry delight protein drink. I hadn't noticed that Mancho happened to be at the counter with his back to me until he turned away from some guy he was visiting with. He tried to get my attention, but I ignored him.

"Hi. You're Marita's friend Suraya, right?" he asked.

"Yes. That's me," I said in a perfunctory manner not wanting to encourage Don Juan. But then the joker in me got the best of me after my silly encounter with Marky. "But some people call me marshmallow."

"Marshmallow! How'd you get that nickname?" he said laughing.

"It's a long story. But basically, I'm friends with someone that says I'm the marshmallow swimming in his hot chocolate jacuzzi."

"Hot chocolate jacuzzi? Sounds like something Willy Wonka would have at his pad. Is your friend Willy Wonka?" Mancho said, starting to get a little fidgety with excitement. Oftentimes, men confuse silliness with flirtation.

"No. He'd be more like Willy Wonka's fun-loving son that's slightly lazy, but one does not need to be too ambitious to be much loved by all. And he is loved by all," I said emphatically and Mancho laughed much amused by the silly talk.

"Sounds like a good friend," Mancho said. "I've seen you here and have been wanting to chat. Marita has spoken highly about you."

"Yeah, I've seen you here too. You like to hold court here at the café counter. I see you upstarts talking more than I see you working out. Are you running for mayor of the gym or something?" I said with a hint of surliness, and he laughed.

"If you were running for mayor I'd vote for you" he said, the charming clown side crawling out of him hoping to get a new fan in me. I laughed. "Would you vote for me?" he asked, boldly flirting.

"I'd have to see what my other choices are."

"I'm the only one on the ballot," he said keeping up the thread of laughter between us.

The café counter waiter handed me my smoothie.

"Well, time to go. Nice meeting you," I said, slipping off the counter stool.

"No, don't go." Mancho pleaded. "We're plotting out my political career." He got up and pulled out the chair next to him and gestured very gentlemanly for me to sit down. "I need your wise counsel. Just stay and chat for a few minutes," he insisted. I raised a wary eyebrow and gave into curiosity to see what he was going to come at me with, since he was obviously a playful sort, but knowing full well I was not interested. I sat down.

"So, what is our campaign slogan going to be?" he asked continuing the charade.

"Oh, now we're campaigning together. Ok. Let me see. We have to talk about the changes we're going to make and how we're going to help the people, right? Isn't that what they all do?"

"Yeah, but I want to do the complete opposite. I want to say that it's all about me and I want the people to help me," he said getting another reluctant laugh out of me. "Ah, I'm just teasing, just joking. So now that we know a little about me, I want to hear about you."

"Like a good politician, I do like to help people," I said.

"Oh, nice. Well, you know maybe you can help me," he said sincerely. "I need help." I was at a total loss as to what this stranger could possibly request my help for.

"Yeah? What's your problem?" I asked.

"I have ED," he said straight-faced.

"What's ED? I asked.

"You don't know what ED is?" he said disappointed.

"No. I have no idea."

He chuckled stymied and swung his legs under the counter stool like a child, bashful and awkwardly, not knowing what to say, as he didn't plan on having to explain the meaning of ED.

"So, what is ED?" I insisted, getting a bit impatient.

"Not so loud," he laughed, trying to put a lid on that which he had unleashed. He leaned into me and looked around and whispered. "It means erectile dysfunction disorder." I let out a whooping, hollering, belly laugh in utter disbelief.

"I'm not going to believe for an instant that you have erectile dysfunction." I was utterly undone in laughter.

"Yes. It's true. I can't get an erection. You like to help people. Maybe you can help me," he said moving up and down in his chair pleased that he was able to continue stirring his pot of mischief.

"You're funny, man. I'm not going to help you with ED. How ridiculous. I'm not a doctor. I can't help you. What a frickin clown you are," I said enjoying his humorous and original approach. "What is this, reverse psychology?"

"No, no it's true!" he insisted, laughing as he tried to get his words out. "It's very sad. Why don't you believe me?"

"Because no one with ED is going to admit it, let along to a stranger."

"You've got a point there," he said.

"Does this buffoonery tactic ever work with anyone?" I asked.
"Sometimes," he had the gall to say, slyly.

"Ah-ha! An admission to your lies, you crazy person." But at this point I was enjoying the creative banter and hutzpah enough, so he won me over as a friend.

"No, lies! Some have tried to help with no success. But I think you may be the one able to help. I have to keep trying. I can't give into a limp dick. You said you like to help people. I'm a person. You can't leave me like this. Don't you want to help me?" he said, reaching for my hand.

"I've got to hand it to you, you're hilarious to think this would work with anyone on any level, but I've thoroughly enjoyed it. I have to go now," I said, as I got up to leave.

"Oh. OK. Well, I'll walk you out," he said, getting up and walking along my side without waiting for a response. He walked me to my car.

"So, what are you going to do?" he asked.

"I'm going home to work," I answered

"What are you working on?"

"I'm writing about my energy body coming to life," I answered.

"Perfect! I want to feel my energy body," he said.

"Oh, no, here we go again. You have enough to work on feeling your physical body, apparently." I stopped at my car. "Here I am. Thanks for walking me out I said wanting to slip away before he tried anymore strange antics. You never know what a clown like him may try to pull. "Well, I had a great time talking with you."

"Can I get a hug?" he asked warmly, apparently softening into his sincere side.

"Sure" I said and gave into his embrace.

"When can I see you next?" he asked with a hint of genuine humility.

"Ah, I don't know," I said, not wanting to have to deal with turning him down and looked around the parking garage evasively. I moved to pull out of his arms but he held me steady and didn't release. He craned his neck around seeking my gaze. I looked him in the eye.

"Why not? What's wrong? I want to see you, take you out on a date," he persisted.

I scrambled around in my mind searching for a response.

"I can't go out with you," I said plainly. His jaw dropped.

"Why not? I'll be good if that's what you're worried about."

"No, it's the opposite. If you wanted to go out with me you certainly didn't pitch yourself well. Why would I want to go out with someone with ED?" And as it came out of my mouth he looked relieved to know it was his own tomfoolery, something he could possibly amend. He laughed.

"Awww, no! You can't say that! You can't use that against me," he said foiled but enjoying the match. He sought my gaze again not wanting to speak until I looked him in his eye. "I feel the ED going away right now," he said suggesting he was getting a boner and pulled me closer into his body.

I pushed away laughing. He tried to hold onto me but I slipped out of his grip, not threatened or upset, just done with the circus show. I headed to the door of my car.

"Well, I truly appreciated speaking with you and I hope I get the opportunity to do so again," he said and kissed my hand.

"You are funny. Gotta go. Bye!" I said laughing and shut the car door. What an introduction to a friendship! What a hilarious come-on! Life is always interesting, to say the least.

11

"The Tantric Sex Match Maker"

As I mentioned, it had dawned on me that perhaps my friend "The Guru Agent" could help me find a sacred sex partner. The Guru Agent was a much older man who could be my father. He had the rare pedigree of being private secretary and promoter for many very famous Gurus and Swamis. He had lived in ashrams all over the world and had the pulse on any new talent in the spiritual adept or healer arena. He was often very instrumental in building the careers and clientele for these spiritual guides from around the world inside the United States. I met him when I was about fourteen and we've been friends ever since.

I called up The Guru Agent and explained in a very blunt and direct way that I was looking for a tantric-sex partner. I insisted that he screen these men for sincerity. They had to be men that he had known over a period of time to be on a spiritual path and truly interested, independently of me, in this sort of exploration. I didn't want someone who just saw it as another kinky sex experiment with an attractive girl. I wanted someone who hopefully had some point of reference for having felt his own energy/body, spiritual self, or at least had a sincere interest in being open to it.

I've never heard the Guru Agent so excited. He was so thrilled to aid me in my quest. The Guru Agent is a businessman and I'd noticed that his business partners were always looking to meet attractive women through him. He seemed to collect women friends for this purpose, I believe. In fact, you could say he is a Guru Agent and Match Maker.

This request couldn't have been more perfect for the little leprechaun of a man that was The Guru Agent. His voice literally changed to a lower, whispery tone as we discussed the parameters of this escapade as if it was the ultimate conspiracy. Maybe it was turning him on, although he seemed pretty asexual even from his own accounts. It did feel like an escapade to put myself out there like this, but doing it through the Guru Agent I figured that I would have more faith in the sincerity of the suitors and they would not take me as a sex addict or crackpot. The Guru Agent and I hashed out the details.

First of all, I had to like this man as a person. I couldn't have sex with any old idiot, no matter what he looked like! I would probably have to get to know him a bit as one would in a regular dating process, although there were no rules as to how long that would be. It could be a few weeks or the first date.

Secondly, I had come to the conclusion that I didn't want a commitment because I had just gotten out of a relationship, but I didn't want someone who was sleeping around with too many people, either. If romantic love feelings grew, I was open for the tantric sex exploration to roll over into a committed relationship and even marriage. Wouldn't that be the perfect twist to the sacred-sex quest?

But the most important rule was that the prospect understood that there had to be incredible communication and total honesty. And being evasive or lying by omission does not count as being honest. I wanted someone who was not afraid to really share his feelings, whatever they may be. This process was about going deeper and getting real. I needed someone that could drop the macho performance and goal-oriented sex to really explore the whole body and the whole emotional spiritual realm. This would take a great ability and desire to be intimate, vulnerable. This sex was about growing and nurturing the kundalini energy and sometimes that could lead to an emotional cathartic moment in which one's partner could not be selfish about their agenda to "get off" or "what turns them on." There had to be the maturity for the journey to lead anywhere: spiritual altered states, communing with Spirit, emotional traumas, lusty sexual awakenings and ecstasy, and possibly even love. They had to be open to all of it as part of the sexual exploration!

The Guru Agent said he already had a few people in mind and would speak to them on my behalf. I was putting myself out there to get what I wanted and I had a sense of great mischief, adventure, and purpose all wrapped up into one. I literally laughed to myself at how humorous this could pan out to be. I was imagining my gleeful, little Guru Agent as he propositioned select suitors, and perhaps their shock, surprise and delight. I wondered how he described me as a person and physically. I wish I could have been listening when he had those conversations. I couldn't believe I was doing this, but the ball had been set in motion and now I waited to hear the responses.

The few friends I told this to laughed and my mother thought I was crazy, but she always seems to get a kick out of my adventures even though she thinks they're a little nutty. She seems to appreciate that I don't lead a dull life and always have some scheme I'm cooking up.

The Guru Agent called me back the very next day with a response. The first contender was a gentleman that traveled the world constantly, a very worldly successful businessman, and he was very excited to meet me. I was told he would call me in a matter of hours. We'll call him the "Silver Fox." The second candidate was, to my surprise, someone I had already met a few times in the past. The first time he was married. The second time I had run into him in an ashram in India when he was going through a divorce.

I remembered we had always had a simpatico, so I already knew that he was a real possibility. He too was a successful businessman and would call me in the next few days. The Guru Agent said he had a few others that he had not heard back from yet.

Sure enough, the first suitor, "The Silver Fox," called! In a very distinguished, low, husky voice he asked for me. His voice in itself was a turn-on. He was very proper, but easy to talk to and we had a few laughs. He very quickly arranged a meeting at the Bel Air Hotel. And so, I was to meet with my first blind tantric date in a couple of days.

I shared my quest with Thad in our next session and he didn't seem the least surprised when I told him about my proactive quest to find someone to explore this new sexual-energy connection that was humming in my being. With a big smile and laughter in his eyes he nodded his head approvingly and said he looked forward to hearing how the selection process went.

I told him that I thought that a good idea would be to have whoever I chose to be my lover come to watch our bodywork sessions together to understand how to help release and encourage the energy to go deeper through the flow and touch of his work. I asked Thad if during a session when I reached a "peak experience" he would be willing to then leave me alone with my prospective sexual partner, at his place, for the tantric exploration to begin. He agreed that would be a good way to teach the chosen one visually to give him an understanding of what it is that I was talking about. He was on board with everything and supportive of how I was inspired to go about it.

The music started and even as Thad just started to breathe, the energy popped open. It seemed like the energy was a racehorse waiting for the gate to spring open so that it could run as fast as it could to a new epiphany for me to experience. It was just under the surface at all times with more and more things to trigger its arousal and bring me into a centered place of love and gratitude for my union with "IT," with "ALL."

I contorted into many positions, releasing pockets of energy and heat held in my body. Then suddenly Thad's hands and the evocative music steered me into a place of quiet and deep surrender. I lay down and lay still, almost too quiet as I traversed from the strong, quick Kundalini breath to a slow, long breath, that landed me in a non-body awareness. It was the blissful breath taking me down into a sensation of stillness, spiraling so deep that I felt I didn't need to breathe! It felt as light as a bite of watermelon, quenching, and sweet. In this place of non-breath, I suddenly felt a luminescent silver light radiate from a new shiny smooth white skin I possessed. Not a human white, but a white like the sheen of white silk.

My limbs, neck, and whole body felt as if they were those of a thinner person and I had the sensation that if I were to move it would be in a fluid, slow, graceful manner as if I didn't even possess joints or bones, but as if I were instead some kind of rubber being. I felt myself as some other creature...an alien creature! I felt my body was going into an arrested state of hibernation, so peaceful and calm it was. I didn't need to breathe in this state!

Then I heard Thad's worried voice whisper in my ear, "Are you O.K.? You are not breathing."

I didn't want to answer for I would have to bring myself out of this most fascinating hibernation. But I could not let him worry, so I mustered an utterance:

"Yes." And it did bring me out of deep hibernation...Rats! I was really going somewhere I'd never been before.

As we sat talking about the day's session, Thad mentioned to me that he really got worried that I wasn't breathing and that when that happened I looked like an ethereal, otherworldly creature, alien-like! He confirmed exactly what I was experiencing and feeling! I don't know what that experience was trying to impart to me. Was this creature another one of my lives in some alternative reality, a past life? I think if I had been allowed to go into my non-breath hibernation state a little longer without being interrupted I would have found myself with some more mind-bending understanding of the entirety of what the being represented. This journey was the true magic of ancient myths!

Some yogis and masters of meditation can go into such deep states that they pull all their life force into their spine and don't need to breathe. These breathless states are called Samadhis. There are different levels of Samadhi you can go to. Samadhi means bliss. And with these different levels of bliss comes greater awareness of who you are. It is said that some of the deeper states of Samadhi resemble a physical state of hibernation; that if you took the pulse of someone in one of these breathless states, they would be pronounced dead.

In India, where the understanding of these different states of awareness comes from, when a yogi wishes to go into a state of deep, breathless Samadhi, he must tell the authorities and take out a permit for the cave he will be using for his Samadhi. This is for the yogi's own protection so that if someone comes across him in his hibernation Samadhi state he will not be mistaken for having died and be buried. I don't know if I was going into a Samadhi state, but the beginning of the breathless state I was slipping into was peacefully sublime.

Now that I had flirted with Samadhi I was ready to go on my blind date. I still am a girl in this reality, so I got myself fluffed up to look pretty flirty: I like to tell people that I'm "Gandhi- Gabor" for the old folks, part Zsa Zsa Gabor and Gandhi, or "Gaga-Gandhi", for the young ins, part Gandhi and part Lady Gaga. I had my make-up, blow-out, nails done and put on a pair of sexy, tight brown leather pants. Unlike Lady Gaga, I still ate my raw meat instead of wearing it. Ha! I was looking pretty LA.

The Bel Air Hotel is nestled in the private residential area with beautiful gardens, swans and a little creek. I walked around the grounds not knowing who to look for, since I had forgotten to ask what The Silver Fox looked like, except that he was an older gentleman.

I suddenly, saw a refined, well-attired portly man with silver hair that was looking inquisitively at me as if he was looking for someone. "No way! This man was too old. He had nice features and pretty blue eyes, but I'd have to call him "The Silver Fat Fox:" to describe him more accurately and not just The Silver Fox.

I was not over the moon at first glance. However, I was there and didn't want to be rude so I figured I'd make the best of it and go through with the date. He was very distinguished looking and after our introduction with an unusual amount of laughter that gave away, we were both very aware of the unusual premises of the meeting. He escorted me to the dining room.

Talk about an elephant in the room. It was not just in the room it was sitting on our heads. Every move, gesture, and word were intently observed by the other, searching for meaning, subtext, and suggestion, to see just what may give way to understanding where the other stood on the matter of partnering up: if, when, how, now, or never. I suppose all dates start out with a similar process of assessment, but in having the specific and foremost intent of finding a tantric sex partner with a blind date, the process was magnified and the tension was way more palpable.

We danced around speaking about the subject directly and in the getting-to-know-you-conversation laughed continuously and I actually really found the Fat Fox fascinating. By the end of the dinner the sexual attraction had us riveted and we didn't want the evening to end. I was shocked by the chemistry that was building with grandpa. I'd never been attracted to someone so old. We spent time flirting in the bar; then we moved out to the gardens and made up silly games. Then we got in his car to go get food someplace else, since we closed down the hotel bar lounge.

On our way back to the hotel he asked me if I wanted to get a room. The brazen lassie that I am I said, "no." I wasn't ready just yet. He parked in a dark street and he kissed me. As I felt his body close I realized he wasn't all fat, as I had perceived, that he had some good muscle to him and he was a marbleized combo of fat and muscle like a fine Kobe beef steak. He went from being the Silver Fat Fox to The Silver Rock Fox.

We made-out for a while and then suddenly he proclaimed: "I haven't felt this way in so long. I want you to totally let go with me. I have to leave tomorrow for two weeks to New York, England, Dubai, and China for business and I want you to come with me. After which I will take you anyplace in the world you want to go. Don't worry about packing luggage you can buy whatever you need along the way. And if all goes well, perhaps, you will come live with me in my castle in Switzerland, be my princess and live happily ever after."

He hugged me tightly and kept whispering in my ear that he hadn't felt this way in such a long time. Then he erupted: "That's it! I'm breaking up with my girlfriend in London for good. She's going to be so mad, but don't worry, she won't try to kill you, I'll make sure of that."

What the heck? I pictured a woman barging into our boudoir with an ax and his muscle and fat marbleized body catching the ax right when it was going to fall on me. Well, he obviously had incredible wealth and lifestyle that would add to the adventure of the affair, a plus. Chemistry, good. Girlfriend, even though she was not an axe murderer--although he wasn't too convincing that she wouldn't be--a deal breaker.

I told him that I would love to travel with him after I finished a six-week course I had signed up for. He couldn't believe that I would turn down his extravagant invitation for a training course, but it was none other than Thad's course for Rule of Four Practitioner Training and nothing was going to stop me from immersing myself deeper into the understanding of this energy awakening. I told him I would be done by Christmas and that we could rendezvous somewhere in the world over the Holidays, if his girlfriend hadn't killed him before that.

He offered to have his chauffeur come to the hotel to drive me home, for it was four in the morning, but I declined and drove off on my own. The evening did not disappoint. Such a shame that the Silver Rock Fat Fox, otherwise known as "grandpa," had a girlfriend. Why can't anything be simple?

He called me the next day asking me to come meet him at the airport and tried to coax me one last time to fly off with him. Unfortunately, I missed the call or I would have gone to see my passionate, rich, lunatic grandpa of a suitor one last time before he was off in his whirlwind life to "axe" his girlfriend who may want to murder me.

12

"The Chainsaw Dialogues"

Brett's place was like a museum of building and tools. It was some crazy never-ending project of theme rooms and colorful mosaic and artwork, bold colored painted walls--very appealing to hippies, children and Dr. Seuss sensibilities.

"Here she is," Brett said handing me a chainsaw.

"It's a she then?" I asked, catching the gender-specific reference.

"Yes. It's a she, all right. I've named her Beulah," he said.

"A good 'ole battle-axe name. A solid woman with a thick arm that wields a rolling pin like a spiked club," I said, and his eyes opened wide, taken aback and he busted up laughing.

"Exactly! You're the only one to get that. Yep! It was either Bertha, Maybel, or Beulah. The kind of Grandma or a Ma from the old days that you didn't mess with," he said, "that could drop the hammer with the best of men if she wanted to."

"So how long have you been building this house?" I asked.

"Forever! Fifteen, twenty years. It's not a house, it's a compound. And it will most likely never end. I like it that way. It's a new meaning to working on your home. It will be done the day I die I suppose," he explained.

"We all have our hobbies and our way of doing things," I said. "I've got to get going soon so I can start on the tree-cutting project, but first I want to invite you to lunch to thank you, if you have the time."

"Oh, that's so nice of you. Well, let me see," he said, looking around his cacophonously colored, preschool-bright living room as if the answer to him accepting the invitation would come from the walls, furniture and fixtures themselves. "Ok, sure. That's real nice of you. You didn't have to do anything. I'm just happy to help. You seem like such a nice girl," he said as he made his way to grab his keys and led us to the door.

There is not much in Topanga in regards to restaurants, so we made our way to a little sandwich store in the woodsy center.

"You can look at the menu and if you don't like anything we can go someplace else," Brett said.

"Hey Suraya!" I heard a familiar African voice yell out from nearby and cringed when it dawned on me to whom the voice belonged. I turned to see the cartoon-happy face of Teltebow, a fixture in Malibu, a poser for life, a fake-it-till-you-make-it kinda guy' that works as a doormat assistant to a famous celebrity but touts that celebrity to be his best friend and claims to be producing one breakthrough album after the next discovering talent and always making some big movie deal.

"Hey, Teltebow!" I said trying to muster up an enthusiastic greeting very unsuccessfully.

"Oh, how funny to run into you way up here. What brings you here?" he asked his eyes settling on Brett, sizing him up for fame or fortune.

"Just borrowing a chainsaw. Doing a little home improvement," I said in a perfunctory singsong manner.

"A chainsaw? Woman, that's not for a petite lady like yourself," he exclaimed, moving into his boisterous pitch and constantly impressing mode.

"I'm here visiting with a friend, but I'm headed back down to work in the studio of one of the biggest movie score producers ever," he said, his chest puffing out.

"Sure, I bet he takes out the trash and runs errands for the guy," I thought to myself. I bet in Africa he was that bamboozler guy that would try to sell you anything from a used paper clip, to your own mother.

"I would like to help connect one of your beautiful projects to one of my people. You know I've worked with top film producers," Teltebow continued to brag.

"Yeah, I know your whole story. You worked with Laddy Da and Lady Paff Fufu," I said, deadpan trying to cut his bragging off at the pass.

"Ahh! Lady Fufu! You're so funny," he said laughing as he searched to read my face to determine if I spoke in truth or jest, but I didn't give him anything to go on, just a blank, easy stare.

"Is there a Lady Paff Fufu?" he asked tentatively. "Who is this person?"

"You mean you don't know of Lady Paff Fufu? I thought you knew everyone famous?" I said teasing. I couldn't believe he didn't know I was joking, but since I had caught the fish, I was going to fry it.

"Oh, nooo I don't. I can't believe it myself!" he said, fully buying the joke. "But you know something funny? In my country one of the staple foods is called Fufu! I love Fufu! It's like a national food. Can you believe it?" he said laughing.

I already knew this fact, that it was a food in Africa, and finally couldn't hold my surly attitude and disdain for this braggart any longer as he had fallen for my Fufu joke. I broke out into laughter with him. Brett seeing me laugh started laughing too. He just sat back for the ride, observing; now that he was a little older and a little slower, he was just going to be in the passenger seat of this encounter.

"Is there really a Lady Fufu?" Teltebow asked incredulously, making us all laugh even more.

"So, this is my friend Brett, the man who is supplying me with a chainsaw," I said to Teltebow. "And this is Teltebow, a man of great connections."

"Hello chainsaw Brett," Teltebow said with that broad, white piano smile of his. Brett shook his hand and nodded.

"And as long as everyone is introducing themselves," a man's voice from behind me spoke out as he approached our group. I turned to be overtaken by a tall, handsome man in his mid-thirties, as he interjected himself into our circle, "I am Wolfgang Von Trapp."

"Like in the Sound of Music," I said, and we all laughed harder as Wolfgang shook hands all around enthusiastically, confidently. The moment Wolfgang grabbed my hand I felt a blush of heat rise up from my hand through my whole body, flushing my cheeks with a fresh swath of pink. This had never happened before. He had my attention, my interest, in an uncomfortable way. He shook my hand with both hands and didn't let it go.

"You're blushing," Wolfgang said softly to me and smiled knowingly.

"Yes, it's hot out here, standing in the direct sun," I said feeling naked as I couldn't hide this sudden overwhelming attraction for a stranger that appeared out of nowhere to hunt me down without mercy.

"I couldn't help but overhear the name of a dear friend of mine, Lady Paff Fufu, a most remarkable woman!" Wolfgang said, looking intensely at me as if no one else was there, still holding my hand and intently sending his desire out to me and feeding off the obvious mutual attraction. I raised my eyebrows in complete surprise and laughed a belly-aching laugh at this jokester's humorous approach to hit on me. "In fact, if you have not met her, it would be my pleasure to introduce you. Lady Paff Fufu doesn't entertain just anybody, but I think she would be most delighted to meet someone as formidable as herself, for it is quite rare to find such a person."

Teltebow's mouth was open and Brett's eyebrows climbed high on his forehead in disbelief.

"I need to meet this Lady Paff Fufu too. I want to bring this great lady the food of her namesake, Fufu," Teltebow said. At this point we were all undone with laughter. Teltebow was laughing, but it was apparent he believed Lady Paff Fufu was a real person of great note, worth meeting.

"This is unbelievable," Brett muttered through his laughter putting his hands on his head incredulously.

"I would like very much to take you to dinner tonight." Wolfgang had the balls to sneak in such a statement in front of everyone in the middle of the comedy mayhem.

"I would like that, but I may be too tired tonight," I said. "Another night?"

"What are you doing that you will be too tired? Perhaps I can help," he said and I felt his longing and affection, the kind that doesn't grow, but is there naturally from the start, just as the heat between us sprung up from the slightest first touch.

"Ah, how sweet! The man wants to help. Just wait 'til you hear what she's doing," Teltebow chimed in.

"She's chopping up trees with a chainsaw," Brett said, finally participating.

"Really?" Wolfgang asked, taken aback and amused.

"Every now and then I like to do home improvement projects to have the wherewithal about these things. Maybe someday I'll want to build my own house," I explained.

"Oh! You're going to build your own house?" Teltebow said, reigniting the laugh fest that was in progress.

"Oh, you are most industrious! I don't know how to use a chainsaw, but we can learn together," Wolfgang said.

"Oh, my gosh! They are going to play with chainsaws on a first date! Now that is truly original, man!" Teltebow said and slapped Wolfgang on the back as if he was an old friend. Although Teltebow was making me laugh, I was starting to wish he would disappear. "He really must like you. I wouldn't chop trees on a first date for anyone. No way, man!"

"Yeah, that is super nice of you," I said to Wolfgang.

"I don't mind if you're a little tired. I will make sure it will be a very relaxing evening afterward," Wolfgang said.

"Yes. Then you can have a good dinner and massage after the chainsaw date," Teltebow kept on his comedy roll. "Or fall asleep as you may be exhausted, or go to the hospital if you chop off a finger by accident in the learning process. Just as long as you are together, right?"

"I prefer to be fresh and put my best foot forward on a first date," I said cracking up at Teltebow's running commentary as I tried to remain sincere with Wolfgang.

"I like you," Wolfgang declared, sincerely, ignoring Teltebow.

"Yes, putting your one foot forward, as you may not have two feet after you chop one foot off," Teltebow said, setting us all off except Wolfgang who kept up the intensity and focus on me and kissed my hand as he handed me his cell phone to enter my number.

"How about tomorrow?" Wolfgang persisted through our laughter.

"That sounds good," I said.

"If she's in one piece still. If you like this guy give up the chainsaw, Suraya. Some men like skinny women, some like them fat, but they all like a whole woman with all their bits intact," big-mouth Tetelbow persisted. "Is this Lady Paff Fufu for real or were you just pulling my leg?" he continued to ramble. "Paff Fufu! Ha! I have to meet her."

After having to resort to the Tantric Sex Matchmaker perhaps my tantric lover had just fallen in my lap in the most bizarre conversation ever. But in moments such as these I always remember Lady Paff Fufu's favorite inspirational saying:

"Live! Live! Live! Life is a banquet and most poor suckers are starving to death."

"Auntie Mame"
(The Movie)

Live! I will! I most indubitably will, Lady Paff Fufu wherever you are!!!

* * *

Bzzzz   I lit up the chainsaw as I stood on the drastic incline of my hill. I had my work goggles and gloves as I always like to be well attired for the job at hand. I pushed it into a tree limb that needed pruning, and the density gave it a kick that the hay bale did not. It snapped me to attention, and I persisted. I had to put a little more muscle into it, a steady push and *voilà*! It sliced right through maintaining all toes and fingers intact, I might add.

I have to say I like a task that makes me feel the strength in whole body, but only when it is by choice, rather than necessary or imposed. I couldn't feel more feminine, but I like to think, even for a day here and there, that I'm capable of surviving in this world at the most basic of physical levels. Again, this curious fantasy of survival led me into another adventure in homesteading arts.

I followed up with a few more tree limbs and in the heat of the day I got thirsty and realized I forgot my water bottle. I traipsed up the hill back to the house and low and behold my ma and pa were in the kitchen. My dad rarely comes in the afternoon, so it was a big surprise.

"Hi Micha!" my dad said, using my nickname. "What are you up to?"

"Hi Litty!" my mom said, using my other nickname and popping back out of the room.

"Oh, just working on a new house project. Planning on finally cutting the trees down for the view."

"That's too much work for you. Let the gardeners do it," said my dad frowning. "How are you going to do it anyway? You can't saw it off!"

"Yeah I can. I can do it with a chainsaw," I said.

"With a chainsaw? You don't know how to use a chainsaw!" Pa said. "Even with a chainsaw, that's hard work."

"Yes. I do know how to work a chainsaw. So, what's wrong with a little hard work?" I said.

"I had a friend growing up called 'Little Johnny Half Foot.' Did I ever tell you that story?" he said, always with a funny story at hand pertinent to the goings-on of the day.

"No. I don't know the story of Little Johnny Half Foot Pa, but I kinda get the idea where you're going to go with this," I said.

"He was a friend growing up in Boise that liked to chop baseballs in half with an axe. I don't know why he liked to do that. But one day he chopped half of his foot off. He ran into his home to tell his mother and she told him to get out of the house because he was making a bloody mess everywhere and staining the carpets," my Pa said laughing.

"Not very nice mother," I said. "Who dubbed him Little Johnny Half Foot?" I asked.

"My brother Dick and I," Pa said.

"Did you call him that to his face, like a nickname?" I asked incredulously.

"Yeah, that became his nickname. He didn't care. He was kinda proud of it," Pa said chuckling in disbelief.

"Times have changed. I can't picture that being OK now," I said.

"He committed suicide years later."

"That's horrible! Why?" I cringed.

"He became a psychologist to try and figure out all his problems, probably from having that horrible mother, and I guess it didn't work," Pa said.

"How sad. Well, he tried," I said.

"He said he had to talk to me about something and we set up a visit. I had to change the date for a business trip to Mexico and when I came back I heard that he had committed suicide. Days later a package arrived with pictures and a letter explaining he wanted to commit suicide. The package was meant to get there before our initial meeting."

"Did he want to meet with you to talk him out of it?" I asked.

"He was reaching out for help, but I didn't know how important it was and it was too late. The package even got there after I came back from Mexico," he said.

"Wow! If he'd talked to you it may have changed everything," I said.

"Well, just don't cut yourself up with the chainsaw or we'll have to call you Little Suraya Half Hand," he said with that morbid sense of humor that we share. We both chuckled.

"That's horrible!" I said laughing.

"Well, we could think of a better name. Little Severed Suraya," he persisted, laughing wickedly.

"So, what are you talking about?" my mom asked all cheery and simple, with the lightness of a little girl as yet unburdened by life's parade of disappointments. Not that she hasn't had disappointments, she was just blessed with the gift of letting the current of life's ever-flowing stream of events carry them away. Burdens do not stick on her, as she is emotionally cleansed daily by her emotional fluidity and perhaps a slight tendency to forgetfulness, which I have come to learn is a good quality to have as we go through life's travails.

"Little Johnny Half Foot," Pa answered.

"Oh, yes that was a terrible story," Mom said. "Are you ready to go to work?" she said to me. "My friend Janet is coming any minute to help trim the tree-vine branches."

"What?! Your friend is coming?" I said clueless.

"Oh, no! Don't tell me you forgot!" my mother said crumpling a bit at her cheery edges.

"You never told me," I insisted.

"You better not be going anyplace. She's coming for you. She's bringing us some large good shears and tools, she says. I told her that you're into doing house repairs yourself and she is inspired with your can-do spirit because she says she's the same," my mom said with a slight plead and a hint of whine in her voice to guilt me, as only sweet non-commanding mothers can do.

"I remember the part of her being impressed and liking my spirit but not that you had booked her for today. But yes, it's fine. I had already planned to do the work today anyway," I assured her.

"Suraya here is planning on trimming the trees with a chainsaw," Pa informed her.

"No Micha! You're crazy. I don't want you doing that! It's not worth it!!" she said. "That's the last thing we need! Now you're going to sever an artery in your arm or leg and they'll have to amputate. You're so vain, you're not going to want to walk around with a big old scar when they sew you back together or you're left missing a limb entirely."

"Oh, no! It's Dr. Doom, again," I said reminding my lighthearted mother of her dark side that has emerged as she has grown older. She instantly goes to the worst-case scenario in regards to any possible health matters.

"Yeah! Dr. Doom!" she reiterated, finding the humor in her handle, knowing there was truth in it and we both laughed. "I don't want you using a chainsaw. Please, don't do it, for me. I just don't want you to make mincemeat of yourself shredding up your beautiful body, not to mention the systemic complication of infections in those cases," Dr. Doom continued relentlessly.

"Ok, Ok. OK. No chainsaw," I agreed begrudgingly. "I can't believe you've gotten so fearful in your older years. We'll have to do it the old-fashioned way, long and arduously in the hot sun," I responded sassily, but acquiescing.

The doorbell rang and my mother went to answer it and greet her friend who was coming, while I rushed out to the yard and down the hill to hide the chainsaw out of plain sight. I didn't want to encourage my mother's worrisome fixation on what she saw as a deadly tool.

Just as I was fitting and securing the chainsaw into the tree branches at the base of a tree I heard my mother with Janet at the edge of the yard.

"It's a beautiful view!" Janet, a tall, lanky, American-heartland woman type, with brown plain-Jane hair cut to her shoulders, in her late forties, stood from the top of the hill with my mother.

Startled by their sudden appearance, I accidentally pulled the chainsaw back, dislodging it from its hiding place and sent it rolling down the steep hill. Shit!

"Hi Litty!" my mother called out and I jumped again. "This is Janet."

"Is there something rolling down the hill?" Janet called out to me, concerned.

"Hi! No! Nothing to worry about," I said covering.

"I see something gaining speed headed to the neighbors," Janet persisted.

"Is it an animal, maybe?" my mom tried to weigh in.

"Well. Yeah, it's just a rock" I said, as good 'ole Beulah, Brett's pride and joy, splashed into the neighbor's pool at the bottom of the hill. I didn't flinch outwardly, but cringed inside.

"Show Janet around and I'll be up in a sec and we'll start the work," I yelled up to them.

"That must be dangerous for the neighbors. I wouldn't want rocks falling into my pool," I heard Janet say as they walked away from the hill's edge.

With surgical precision I scrambled down the steep hill, hopped down the neighbor's wall and jumped into the pool to fish out the chainsaw. I didn't even look to see if the neighbors were looking out their window and could catch sight of me. I just felt an urgency to get the dangerous tool out of their pool before they had time to ask how it got there. Poor Beulah took a tumble, in my effort to hide her from my mother, that risked chopping up a few animals and causing injuries to the neighbors. I'm glad Beulah couldn't speak to complain of her misadventure at my hands like the child that rats on the new babysitter for almost accidentally blowing up her employer's house.

I scrambled back up the tiresome slope with Beulah.

"Hi Litty!" I heard my mother's voice again but this time it was on the hillside steps leading to the deck. Oh, no! Now I would be caught red handed with Beulah and be embarrassed. Instinctively, I released the contraband chainsaw so as not to be caught, and it rolled back down the hill. Hell!

"It's so peaceful down here. The deer come by every afternoon in the spring and summer," my mom said to Janet.

"I see something rolling down the hill again," Janet pointed out behind me.

"The dirt is loose down here. It's probably another rock. I'll be up the hill in a minute to start work," I said, as I turned back down to get the chainsaw again! Damn it! All this trouble and I really didn't have to hide the chainsaw from anyone. I can be totally honest with my mother so I don't know why I was creating mayhem for myself to avoid a little harping. It's funny how old parent-child dynamics crop up even when one is an adult.

"Thank you so much for helping us out!" I said to Janet as we clipped thick vines around the house with long-handled sheers. Oh, the tedium of it compared to the power and efficiency of the waterlogged Beulah! I wondered if she still ran properly. I'd have to check later.

"My pleasure. I like to support a fellow independent woman. If we band together, we can do anything," she said, full of principle anyone could admire.

We spent the long, hot afternoon chatting and cutting, making headway the old-fashioned way. I had visions of being from the pioneer days when neighbors helped each other out more and depended on one another for the basics of life. I enjoyed the brief fantasy. There was something wholesome to it.

"Bye everyone!" my dad said, as he walked carrying his typical four bags of newspapers, vitamins, a computer, and dragging his little poodle Gaston by the leash. He looked like a happy hobo as he tossed everything into his already full car. I walked over to his car to say goodbye.

"Pa, you never told me why Little Johnny Half Foot killed himself."

"He was lonely and couldn't take it. Loneliness burns holes in some people even when they're surrounded by people all the time, others are happy to be alone and don't feel alone even when they never see people and live way out in some remote place, in fact they can't stand too many people. Some people are just troubled. They're too delicate for life, and give up."

"Did it spin you into an existential crisis about life after death? Did you feel his spirit around you?" I asked.

"Did I feel his spirit? Ha! No!" he said laughing. "I don't think about such things as life after death and God. It's a waste of time. I'll find out what happens when I die," he said, dismissing the matter. "Looks like you guys are making good progress!" Pa yelled out. "It was a good thing you listened to your mother and will leave the chainsaw tree-trimming to the experts."

"Can you believe my crazy daughter wanted to cut the bigger tree limbs down the hill with a chainsaw all by herself?" my mother politely exclaimed disapprovingly. Then laughed. Janet looked at me square on, accessing the prospects of what she was hearing.

"Oh, I'm sure she can handle the chainsaw fine. But I guess it's better to be on the cautious side," Janet said factually, confidently, admiringly.

"Good stories Pa," I said, giving him the blessing to leave, but he didn't seem ready to stop reminiscing yet . . .

"I have an apropos story for you...." my pa started in again.

I never think: Oh, no, there he goes again with the stories! These are the moments I get to know him and in essence understand myself. I need to know him just as much as I need to know the story of divine cosmic beginnings from whence we all manifest.

It's amazing how one minute I'm expanding into the arms of the ALL – the universe – through fiery channels of bliss coursing through every cell and then yet, the next minute I'm captivated to understand my father and still care about the life of a man, Little Johnny Half Foot, who I never knew. It still mattered to hear the details of our little lives even though the expanded perception I was coming to know more and more frequently seemed to be of the greatest importance and plugged me into the greatest power I've ever known, an energy I was coming to know as God!

I have learned that the large does not take away the importance of the small, it adds to it always. It is never about replacing or transcending. It is always about expanding the repertoire of layered understanding. For me it was as if I'd been given new colors to paint the scene of a larger landscape of the Whole Life experience that was revealing itself to me. That never means I don't paint with the old colors. Now I just have a bigger palette in my hand to create life with.

Somehow the small details of the earthly life matter more, not in a heavy way, for at times I feel that I am becoming lighter than a feather. It has given every aspect of life a new layer of experience. Food tastes more satisfying, colors can feed me, music can be healing and all the senses are a doorway to an altered peak state. It is how the extremes, from divine states to earthly routine and the knowing and conveying of it all mix together to actualize my gifts and potential for love in this life.

And people see me mostly as they always have, except for the new spark they catch occasionally, or maybe my laughter is that of a stoned man completely carefree. However, my inner world is radically changing, proving the wisest saying ever said, "Perception is reality." Somewhere between these perceptions I try to inhale the truth one breath, one laugh, one story at a time.

My Pa continued his story and I was aware of a feeling in my body. The map of his life overlaid on mine, pointing out and marking certain key landmarks in the terrain of my heart that showed how I got to be the take-charge tree-chopping lassie that I am. And just as the greatest of the cosmos fills me with love and belonging, this little story makes me feel love and connection, and pride too. The threads that create the person I am with my perceptions and sensibilities come reaching from both the vast mysterious void of spirit and through my earthly ancestral lineage. Then it is the needle of love that pierces through our earthly heart and spins together these two threads of our creation to give meaning to life.

My Pa continued,

"…At the lodge up at Warm Lake, Idaho, it was my job to upkeep things. Both Dick, my brother, and I did a lot of renovations. Dad gave us a free hand. He trusted us. One time I decided this giant tree was ruining the cabins' view of the lake so I chopped it down. I miscalculated the way the tree would fall and it fell on my dad's pickup truck and completely smashed the roof in," he said laughing hysterically.

"What did your dad say?" I asked laughing along with him.

"He came running out when he heard the crash and just stared dumbfounded and said 'Gosh almighty!' He never got mad. Didn't say another word. We didn't get in trouble. He just had to buy a new car," my Pa said reminiscing. "Anyhow, better leave some things to the experts, but I like your spirit."

"Thanks Pa! Can't believe grandpa didn't get mad," I said pondering over a parent's great patience.

"He had given us the reins to make decisions like that, so what could he say?" he said, reminding me of the great confidence he's always had in me, which included trusting me to make big decisions as a child where I too could fuck up. "Bye everyone!" My dad yelled out a final farewell as he waved and backed out of the driveway in his car.

The vines and trees were trimmed by sunset and the "pioneer ladies of self-sufficiency" were exhausted, beat. All I could think is that I never would cut trees again! I was so glad I had not accepted Wolfgang's invitation for dinner, as pioneers go to bed early after a long, hard-day's work under the hot sun.

New friends, rich stories, greater connection, new possibilities of a tantric lover; who would've imagined a chainsaw would come with a world of gifts!?

13

"Waking the Tiger"

"Do you ever feel lonely?" Thad asked me as I sat totally contented in a chair still sweaty after his hot-box yoga class.

"No. I feel too full of the Life Force Energy to be lonely," I replied. I noticed a very contemplative look in Thad's face. It seemed so out of the blue. I thought he must have been feeling lonely and wanted to see if I could commiserate.

"Huh," he responded and walked away. I was surprised that Thad would be lonely. All I felt from the openings I had through his work was self-satisfaction and an ever-deepening, overwhelming love continuing to grow that made me feel full and content.

Was he not experiencing what I was experiencing from this spiritual practice we shared? Perhaps what I was experiencing would not last and I too would feel that loneliness again. Perhaps I still had hopes of finding a real match and he didn't anymore. Nothing more was said about his question for a long time, but it stayed with me. Perhaps it wasn't so easy to find a tantric relationship and it isn't enough to just marinate in the bliss of self on this earth plane without a companion.

Thad's course on bodywork training called "Rule of Four" began. There were about ten women and two men and we all sat in a circle and introduced ourselves. He handed out a lot of literature: Freud, Gopi Krishna, Jung, Ken Wilbur, Stanislav Grof, Peter Levine, Donald Kalshed, Jack Kornfield, Abraham Maslow, Grey's Anatomy to understand the muscles, handouts that explained the chakras that correspond to the muscles and the corresponding emotions that tend to be held in those areas.

I was in heaven and on fire. I'm on fire so much in this book some-one should call the fire department to douse me. The literature spoke of everything I was going through and confirmed so many epiphanies that were bubbling up from inside. It helped me understand more in depth the process I was going through from people who had been researching the subject of trauma held in the body, spiritual evolution, altered states for healing, the secrets both dark and enlightening held in the subconscious, and how to open up to it, all in an attempt to reclaim one's wholeness – to be fully alive and thrive!

Stanislav Grof, through his work that involved LSD therapy, saw recurrent patterns of trauma or pleasure in one's life that begin at birth and are compounded every time they surface, creating a deeper reactionary sense memory. He called it the COEX System and defined it as a specific constellation of memories consisting of condensed experiences (and related fantasies) from life periods of an individual. The memories belonging to a particular COEX System have a similar basic theme or contain similar elements and are associated with a strong emotional charge of the same quality. The nature of these themes varies considerably from one COEX system to another. For example, a particular system can contain all memories of the past exposures of an individual to humiliating and degrading situations that have damaged self-esteem. Others depict sex as dangerous or disgusting, and yet another COEX constellation may be of the safety, love, and approval, a memory first rooted when breastfeeding by a warm, peaceful, and loving mother. Basically, this is why some "issues" carry such a big charge, because they are compounded by a group of associations that reinforce the original trauma or positive life experiences over time.

Grof said that many LSD therapy sessions would take people back in time to these traumatic events and the patient could then experience how every time the trauma came up, things, colors, smells, people, or a similar emotional trauma, it would imprint as added triggers to the trauma, creating more irrational subconscious triggers that would set off the trauma. Then a person would find himself in a bad mood, reliving a compounded ball of emotions: fear, hopelessness, etc., reliving the original trauma from something as irrational as the color red. And that color red would not just bring up the root trauma, but all subsequent similar emotional events that compounded the trauma into one big, highly charged emotional ball of wax.

However, this is all subconscious and all that the individual knows is that he finds himself feeling very insecure around his new, lovely girlfriend whose favorite color is red. How can anybody live fully in the moment when one is at the mercy of these subconscious triggers? The insecure lover will then not understand why he loves his girlfriend, but can't stand to be around her at times for no apparent reason. The subconscious seems to be so strangely programmable.

An extreme example of trauma and the way the subconscious works in this manner is portrayed in the movie "Sybil," starring Sally Fields. Colors and other innocuous things would trigger Sybil's trauma from extreme abuse and catapult her into one of her multiple personalities to avoid the memory of the unthinkable abuse she experienced.

The idea of the COEX System helped explain why the recurrent tightness in my throat, "the poisoned apple" episode, and pain in my heart that made me feel as if I was being crucified seemed to be so layered. The pain and tightness were my somatic symptoms forcing me to remember the different episodes, reasons, and associations that had lumped into tightness in my throat that revolved around the toxic programming that shut me off to my heart. This is the great intelligence of the body. It will not let you get away with living half-heartedly. It will find a way to speak to us and get our attention, but it is up to us to find a way that enables us to understand what it is saying to us.

Grof says that the most important part of the COEX System is the core, or initial experience that was registered in the brain and laid the foundation for a specific COEX System. My gut tells me that there is still a block from farther back in my childhood that I have not become aware of yet, before this particular "tight throat" COEX System is cleared. The process of unwinding may be a little slower without the LSD, but in my case, the openings and lessons were happening so naturally and often, that they consumed much of my time. Maybe I don't need LSD.

Peter Levine, also in the vanguard in the world of understanding the psyche and trauma, coined another name for a similar concept to Grof's COEX System, called "Traumatic Coupling." In Traumatic Coupling, specific stimulus is so strongly linked to a particular response that together they override normal response and behaviors. Metaphorically, every time you eat, smell, or see turkey, you experience eating a club sandwich of pain.

Levine gives an example of administering the drug Yohimbine, which increases the heart rate and blood pressure. The members of the non-traumatized group of people simply experienced straightforward sensations in their body, whereas when the drug was given to a group of war veterans suffering from post-traumatic stress disorder, the body sensations induced them to re-experience the terror and horrors of the battlefield. Those specific body sensations of arousal through increased heart rate and blood pressure are so linked to the trauma-emotion response of terror, horror, rage, and helplessness that the traumatized persons can't help but re-experience those feelings, even when evoked by something that is normally pleasurable.

Levine says that a common example occurs when traumatized individuals panic when sexually aroused. In sexual arousal, some of the physiological responses such as heartbeat, etc., trigger panic, immobility and helplessness, rather than intense enjoyment. This may lead people to believe that they have been sexually abused when in fact their reaction is due to the body's sensations that are reminding them of another trauma having nothing to do with sex. One may say that it is an illogical and most defective system, but there is an intelligence operating there that brings attention to the fact that one has not fully confronted and released a trauma. The part of us that has been shut down by the trauma manifests itself as these symptoms, demanding us to take action to bring our whole being fully back to life!

I did not have dramatic physical traumas, but I still had some programming that shut me down to the totality of my feelings and acceptance of who I am that had prevented me from experiencing the love and joy that my being was capable of. Everyone's bar is different, but we all have something to work out. The mystery of mysteries is the vastness and workings of the psyche and subconscious. It truly is a strange wonder what is filed in there. The higher self and bliss seems to be in there too.

"You're going to be working on each person here at one point throughout the course," Thad announced. Yeech! It didn't seem appealing to me to touch some of these people in the room. I guess I was only used to touching those with whom I was sexually involved or family and close friends. I'm so spiritual and have all this universal love, but I was somewhat disgusted by the idea of touching some of these strangers. Ha! I looked the group over again and thought the older lady, Marion, who had a nervous unsettledness about her and a sickly grey demeanor, was the person I had the biggest aversion to in the class and would be my least favorite person to work on for the first session.

"Suraya, you pair up with Marion." I cringed. How was I going to do a good job on someone that yeeched me? How would I hold the interest to provide the compassionate healing and "holding space" for someone I wanted to keep my "space" from in regards to distance? "Holding Space" in this work means being present, bearing witness to someone's cathartic experience.

We set up the tables and of course I was sweet to her and determined to fake the caring as much as my acting ability allowed. She lay looking very ready to soak in the massage and receive. She hadn't a clue as to my feelings, thank God.

I approached the table, when suddenly the kundalini heat in me started to rise spontaneously. I hadn't evoked it in some kind of mental prayer or anything. I was just thinking about doing the bodywork sequence correctly. I became so hot, I started to sweat and as I felt the heat, my energy currents began to tangibly run through my body and my hands. Then it was as if I stepped into a bubble of love and compassion that transformed my feelings toward Marion. I had a total consciousness shift and this old, brittle woman who I found so distasteful had become my dearest beloved child – all things were equal.

As I touched Marion with the compassion, I felt it became a most pleasurable experience for me. The heat seemed to quicken the flow of energy in my body and this was inspiring me to work my hands over her as if I was in an energy dance with her.

"Ooh, that feels really good," she moaned. "Oooh, that is a spot…that's good, ooooh!" Marion started to cry and shake.

"Are you O.K.? What are you feeling?" I asked. She didn't answer. "Should I keep working on you?" She nodded.

I kept working on her and she just kept crying. I pressed into her gently not deeply as before so as not to stimulate too much more emotion, for she looked like she was experiencing enough stuff coming up. I alternated with gentle caresses as Thad had told us. This was to let the body take a break and know that it would be pleasurable and not just painful, so that there is trust in opening up deeper. Marion started wailing. What had I done? This is the time when you just are present and "hold space" to allow the cathartic experience to run its course. Thad came over to speak to Marion,

"What are you feeling?"

"Pain. It's like a huge endless void." She sobbed with her eyes shut tight. I noticed she never opened her eyes throughout the experience. It was as if she was lost someplace else, seeing through other eyes, another time and place. She had left the room to see the dangerous dungeon her soul was trapped in.

"What is the pain from?" Thad continued.

"I don't know. It's all over my body." Marion eeked out the words through her sobs, hopelessly.

"Is there any resource you can find? Something that will remind you of the pleasure you've experienced in life and give you comfort that it's going to be O.K. when the pain passes?" Thad asked, guiding her toward the light at the end of her dark tunnel of emotional memory into which she was trapped.

"No! There is only endless pain," she cried.

What? I was astounded that she couldn't find any resource. It opened me up to the possibility of a pain that I had not yet known. Regardless of the depths of my pain or despair, I always have had a feeling that everything in the end will be O.K. and that I will somehow be taken care of no matter what I have had to endure! Perhaps this is part of one of my positive COEX System memories imparted to me by my mother or maybe I do have an understanding of a higher-self watching over me that gives me this security. Watching Marion made me see there was a world of trauma that I was not aware of.

Well, as usual, we had to wrap up our session due to class-time constraints, just when it was getting so intense. Thad instructed me to continue the loving caresses. I was relieved to bring her back since I'd helped her open this chasm and wanted to make sure she got out. There is a real responsibility with this work. I caressed and held her face hoping the love that engulfed me would encompass her. I rocked her.

"Do you like the way she is touching you?" Thad asked.

"Yes. I'm so grateful for it." She still was sobbing, but it had shifted to a sob of gratitude and then her being started to move into a place where she could let the love in. She grabbed on to me to express her great appreciation. She smiled and looked relieved.

"You're an angel," she said. "Thank you, thank you..."

This really works. I felt an emotional high as I do after bathed in the Kundalini opening. The heat and intensity of the kundalini subsided and I no longer looked at anyone in the class with an aversion to working on them, for the work itself evoked so much love, compassion, and beauty in me, that it was a pleasure. However, stepping back in my mundane perspective of life I was glad to not have to work on Marion again because she's a real piece of work! This can be a little scary for a novice. My God! She has no resources of positive memories to evoke in the midst of her trauma to help her through!

Looking at Marion across the room sitting up in the closing circle, she looked reborn, cleansed. She reflected softness and light instead of the brittle edginess she had before. I was so happy to be a part of it.

The intellect is only part of a myriad of intelligences that need to be incorporated and summoned to work out the obstacles in our life. The mere process of acknowledging that these other types of intelligence exist, recruits new resources and abilities from our "whole being." This shines the spotlight on the inner-world that is guiding us to reach our whole potential as divine human beings.

We'd like the journey to be as soft as purring kittens, and sometimes it will be, but as you can see from my experience so far and from Marion's experience, this work can be overwhelming to the emotions and can stir both pain and pleasure. That is why Peter Levine calls this journey that peers into the subconscious: "Waking the Tiger."

14

"Elbow Blow Job"

I dreamt I was dancing in a ball gown with Wolfgang, full of youth and juicy readiness for love and engaging in sensual mysteries with a very masculine man that he is and is my dream man. I felt my energy rise up through my skin and glow like a sheen of glitter as it reached out to meet him. The ballroom was ornate and regal and as we sailed back and forth across the floor. It was like a Disney animated movie where the heroine finally meets her prince and all is well and put right again in the kingdom after it was freed from a spell of darkness in which everyone's true and good nature was tested. But in the midst of the perfection there was a feeling that I was not able to be fully present because my mind was searching for something I needed desperately to remember. I couldn't remember the trials of darkness I had to overcome, that broke the evil spell and brought back to life this magical kingdom and blissful love.

Then the lioness that had appeared in my dream before the kundalini awakening, leapt down from the balcony, but no one seemed to be disturbed. It paced around the edge of the ballroom and although I felt love for the animal and did not fear it, I did not want it to get closer, for I knew if it came up to me it would be to take me away from this dream. It would end the vision of love with Wolfgang. It was then that I noticed the lioness would walk past partygoers and they wouldn't even glance at it. No one could see the lioness but me.

I woke up in a troubled sweat, for although the dream was smooth and halcyonic and full of love, the same unease that there was something that I needed to desperately remember stayed brewing in the back of my mind. I was worried that if I was not conscious enough to remember, I would not be able to retrieve the wisdom that knows how to battle the destructive forces in life that threaten the potential happiness life can offer.

This was the third time the lioness had come to me, every time watching, waiting to take me away, but where? She is my inner world guiding me. Perhaps there to take me away from old patterns and habits that would steer me away from my new path. It was my spirit watcher unleashed to protect me from my shadow self, it occurred to me. Only time would unravel the mystery of the recurrent dreams of the lioness in my life. On this path all things were revealing themselves quickly and all things had reason and purpose, so I just needed to give it time.

I thought about the dream often enough, so I felt a need to write it down and with that gesture, I filed it for the future as a warning from the mystical messenger that was guiding me, The Life Force Energy, that I needed to figure out how to heed, once I could better understand the dream world's symbolic language. The lingering feeling of helplessness the dream inspired dissipated like a light morning fog. Then the excitement of my real date with Wolfgang filled my mood. The evening couldn't come quickly enough!

"Ding Dong!" Oh, jees, Wolfgang was at the door. In an instant, thoughts shot through my head: this was a real possibility, he was the right age, he wasn't a widower, he seemed worldly, and he was classically handsome with a rugged ease about him that gave him the manly quality that I seek in a mate.

I answered the door. "Hi," I said. We just stared at each other for a second and smiled. I focused on his healthy rosy cheeks and felt my cheeks flush as if I had a light sunburn.

"You look beautiful!" he said and we just smiled at each other some more, like a couple of dopes. "Shall we?" he said and offered me his arm.

We drove up into the Malibu Mountains to a famous restaurant called Saddle Peak Lodge, an old cabin lodge in the mountains that was transformed into a cozy and romantic restaurant. It is famous for its wild-game theme.

The deer and moose and buffalo on the walls stared at us as our conversation bounced around from subject to topic seamlessly. I forgot about my tantric quest, but not about sex, for the attraction kept us buoyantly floating safely on the surface of the deep waters of sexual possibility. However, through the evening, although the twinkle in his eyes and the glee in his smile spoke volumes, he didn't try to hold my hand or lean over to kiss me as some men do when the attraction is so thick, it can be cut with a knife.

"Power, power, power...there are so many kinds of power," I mused out loud in a stream of consciousness. I was thinking of the sexual magnetism between us. The kind you cannot resist. But tonight, unlike the rest of my tantric quest, I could not bring myself to mention it out loud so honestly, so matter-of-factly.

"Yessss! I know what you mean." He looked at me slyly, playfully.

"Yeah. What do you think I mean?" I asked.

"Well, there is power in doing anything well, great, the best. Then people seek you for your skill. And if it is something of great need to others, it gives one the ability to command great favors or wealth. Then there is the power of the heart that loves greatly and bestows great altruistic gifts, such as has been shown through people like Mother Teresa, or Gandhi, or Jesus. They command people through love to rise up and sacrifice even their own lives, for the good of humanity. Then there is the power of charismatic lunatics who through lies and manipulation know how to almost hypnotize less conscious individuals, whip them up and rally them to great destructive deeds. We all know the power of money, as in it can buy anything, even people; or the power of he who carries the biggest stick, fire power, or military force."

"That's a pretty good run down of the different meanings of power," I said. "Some say life is a struggle or a desire for power, whichever power you choose to vie for; the kind of power you value most. What kind of power do you value most?" I asked.

"Yes, power is an excellent subject. There is another power that I'm most interested in, more than my individual power, more than those we've mentioned. I'm more interested in the power between you and me. Do you feel it?" he asked, as the whole wattage of his being seemed to grow in density, vibrancy, and yes, power.

"Do I feel what?" I said, feeling a little stupid that I was playing stupid by not wanting to acknowledge the power between us, the power he had over me, just yet. I felt a deep tremor and throb of excitement go through my body that set off a wave of humming-bird quick shaking that was so fast, it quaked though me like a shiver.

"Ha!" He laughed and took a long swig of his drink, all while he gave me a piercing, steady stare, letting me know that he thought I was lying and that I felt exactly what he was talking about. His stare made me even hotter under the collar, but I held my pretense for the fun of the game and squashed my shivers so that they were imperceptible. I wondered what I was doing, playing a little hard to get when I was actively and openly looking for my tantric lover. But it was fun and a good tension builder. I would confess at the right moment my true feelings and desires. I continued to eat calmly, but was dying inside.

We enjoyed our chatter so much, that we closed the restaurant down. We weren't aware that we were the last ones left until we noticed the waiters setting the tables for the next day.

"Let's go sit by the fire. I'm a little cold," I suggested.

We sat at a freshly set table in front of the fire. It very quickly got too hot, but not wanting to move tables again, I looked for some relief. I picked up the spoon and feeling it cold to the touch put it on my cheek. I traced the spoon around my face to my sensual delight.

"Oh, this feels so good. You have to try it," I said. "Here, let me do it to you. He leaned forward in his chair and I took the cold metal spoon and traced up the inside of his forearm. He shivered.

"Now let me do your face," I suggested. He leaned in further and closed his eyes and I traced the spoon on his face. I'm sure the waiters who watched us out of the corner of their eyes were not too pleased with us dirtying up the clean silverware, but they just continued to busy themselves in the background pretending that they weren't witnessing a silverware seduction.

"Mmmmm. You're right. This is amazing. Let me do it to you," he said and picked up a spoon of his own. He traced my face, my lips and then took the spoon to trace my bare inner thighs--as I had a miniskirt on--right up to where my thigh meets my crotch, but stopped there. Daring, hot move. Inside my mind I applauded Wolfgang's boldness and willingness to join in the play.

The cool metal on my thighs while sitting by the fire was very sensually erotic. The silverware would soak up the body heat and get warm so we would have to trade it up with another piece of cold cutlery; a butter knife, a fork, yet another spoon, all were culinary tools of sexual excitement. It's a good thing we weren't in the kitchen, or God knows what other culinary tools we would have rubbed on each other.

Finally, our table full of silverware was warm, worn, and we had exhausted our cool sensation of options, so we got up to leave.

"You have amazing silverware," Wolfgang said to the waiters with a knowing smile as we departed. We giggled as we left and a few waiters nodded happily, but appropriately and professionally held back their laughter.

"If I had a cold spoon I'd spoon you all the way home," Wolfgang said and we both busted up laughing.

"And if I had a cold fork I'd fork you all the way home" I said, joining in the merriment.

"Let's not let the evening end. Come to my house. Just to talk. We don't have to do anything. I promise you'll be safe," Wolfgang said. I agreed and we drove back through the mountains to his beautiful home on the cliffs of Malibu overlooking the ocean.

We sat inside his outdoor living room with a marvelous ocean view and he served me tea, as I do not like alcohol, and he sat in front of a big pitcher of water.

"Now that the trail by cutlery has forced you not by words but by deeds to admit you feel the power between us, I want to ask you a question," he said, making me laugh at his silliness. "Did you really not feel anything when I first asked you in the car?" he asked, letting the innocence of a little boy side peek out of his in-control-and-command character that projected a man that could not be fooled easily. His manner of asking let it be known that he cared.

I couldn't hold back my shy excitement and cracked a smile.

"Yes. I feel the power," I said and he sprung into glee and relief.

"Good! That's so good! I knew it!" he said. "Hey, you tried to tease me in not a good way. You did not tease me. You tortured me a bit," he said with surges of real emotion. "And now I want to ask you something else." He paused. "But you can't tease me this time. You have to be straight."

"O.K. what is it?" I said, feeling his intense stare like a glaring light I had to avert my eyes from, but I did not. I held the stare.

"I ask you directly because we don't know each other long and I really like you."

"Now you're making me nervous," I said. He paused again and looked at me with electricity circulating in his eyes waiting to plug into me and light me up.

"Will you make love with me? Have sex with me?" he said boldly laying it out on the line with sincerity and humility. It surprised me that a worldly man would put it on the table instead of trying to seductively lead me down the path with charm and persistence. "He must have a good heart," I thought. I appreciated his caring. My answer welled up in me and came out without much thinking.

"Yes!" I said almost proudly, as if I was able to give him a great gift, filled with pride that I was the gift in his eyes. He picked up the full pitcher of water on the table and dumped it over his head in one swoosh.

"Wooohoo!" he exclaimed through the water. "It's too hot I had to cool myself down. I laughed so hard at his unexpected display of excitement. "Let me take you upstairs." He grabbed my hand and danced me around toward the stairs. Then he ran up the stairs and slid back down the banister toward me and jumped off victoriously. "Wooohoo!" I continued to laugh in total disbelief of his childlike exuberance. Perhaps that is why I dreamt we were dancing in a Disney cartoon. I was tuning into his very-much-alive inner child.

He took me by the hand kissing it and led me upstairs. We walked into his bedroom and he stopped us in front of the bed and just caressed my face and hair, standing inches away.

"Yes?" He asked again not just wanting assurance but wanting to hear me say it as it seemed to turn him on so.

"Yes," I said hardly able to speak. I was overwhelmed with all of Wolfgang's theatrics while he was walking me toward my first sexual experience since I had broken up with Double Double with Cheese. It had been a while, since the relationship was sexless in the end.

He finally grabbed the back of my head and pulled me in for our first kiss. It was long and deep and had the effect of arresting all thoughts. Then it was on. As we kissed greedily, his hands undressed me. He unzipped my skirt and pulled it down. He did so as he moved forward on me and the skirt at my ankles bound me in such a way, I was too restricted to take a few steps and turned to meet the ground as I fell. Before I could take a full breath, he dove into me from behind and like a crack marksman, hit the bull's eye. It was a risky move where someone could've gotten hurt, but miraculously it occurred like a masterfully executed move.

We moved together into shapes geometry has not discovered, or not named yet, and chiropractic medicine would not advise. We had it out, the two of us pushing to be inside the other. When the lust dust cleared a bit and we lay at rest in each other's arms, we were speechless at first. But soon we broke out into a lively conversation as if we were old friends. There was a fit here, no doubt.

I had found my tantric lover!! And maybe so much more!

In the midst of this good post-coital simpatico, I suddenly got a lusty desire to lick and bite Wolfgang's armpit and elbow. It was the kundalini intuitions kicking in I could tell by the quality of the energetic pull--a pull and desire I have never had before, for I do not have a fetish or proclivity for elbow or armpit.

So, in the middle of his sentence I went with my unique inspiration. I didn't ask him if I could make out with his armpit, like he asked me if I wanted to have sex. I wasn't going to give him the opportunity to think. I felt the flow of inspiration and I was going to ride it. This was the tantric exploration I was seeking and I was going to allow the stream to carry me where it might.

I began to lick and bite his shoulder. I grabbed his arm and pinned it over his head and went to town licking and biting his armpit.

"Oh, ah! What are you doing?" Wolfgang asked as if I had a special plan and I knew what I was doing.

"I just had a sudden intense urge for your arm. A sudden lusty desire called to me to be satisfied through your arm," I explained, truly unsure how he would take it. But who cared? There was magic for such a new and different desire to pop up like that, so it was worth exploring the new body wisdom burgeoning through me.

"Yeah? Oh! Wow! It feels really amazing."

I licked and bit and lusted my way down his arm to his elbow.

"Wow! That's amazing!" he said, with a quick burst of laughter lost in arousal.

The sexual satisfaction I felt in lustfully isolating, servicing, pleasuring this unique part of his body was instant gratification and at the same time it fed and perpetuated the building sexual intensity of the act.

"That's amazing!" he exclaimed, as if he was ascending to a new beatific view from which to see the mortal world. "I'm beginning to see colors!"

"Wow, he is a sensitive one," I thought to myself. Well, I was not seeing colors but lusting after an elbow and an armpit. And that was miraculous enough at that moment for me. I told myself not to think, just let go.

I worked in his inner arm and biceps a bit to let it build a little slower, a valley to reflect and rest in between the peeks of new experience.

"Oh, my God, I almost came," he declared.

I plunged my face into his armpit, my mouth working like a fish during a feeding frenzy.

"Oh, Oh, Oh! The colors again!" he said quivering. I quickly skipped down to the middle of his hard bicep and then attacked his elbow to continue the feeding frenzy.

"Ah! Ah! Ha!" Wolfgang gulped and breathed his exclamations as he came on his stomach into the rainbow of colors behind his eyes. I softly licked his elbow to ease out of the intense physical contact and plopped into the very armpit I had my way with.

"What was that? Where did you learn that?" he asked befuddled. I laughed.

"No one taught me to lick and bite armpits and elbows," I said laughing. He laughed too. "I've never done that or felt inspired to do that before. It just suddenly hit me out of the blue for the first time and so I went with it."

"I'm glad you did! Wow! I've never seen colors during sex before. What I'm saying is I've never seen colors like auras. No one has ever done that before. I didn't know my elbow and armpits were so sensitive or sexual for me. Like a new erogenous zone," he said astonished. Then he went into an Irish leprechaun voice "Aye lassie, there is a pot of gold at the end of the rainbow. I knew it!" We both cramped in laughter.

"I think my body wisdom picked up on what specifically would turn you on at this specific moment, so it guided me to desire that part of your body that would unlock your energy to move and open you spiritually. Like I said, I never have found an armpit or elbow so delicious and make me so horny before, ever!" And we both laughed in spooky amazement.

"Yeah, me neither," he said blown away and continued laughing. "But what is this body wisdom that you say guides you?"

"I had a spiritual opening, very energetic. I feel energy different in my body now and it guides me. It actually is guiding me to seek my tantric lover."

"What is a tantric lover? Can I be your tantric lover?" He asked.

"Yes, you can. In fact, I was going to ask you if you would be my tantric lover to explore opening each other up sexually and spiritually. You're a natural" I said, lowering my voice in quiet sincerity, since we had been laughing so much, I didn't want him to think it was not important and real.

"Yes. I will be your tantric lover. I will be whatever you want to be," he said in a sexual haze. "Is tantra power between us?" he asked, pleased with himself. I chuckled.

"Well, I hadn't thought of it like that, but I guess it is the power between us. Tantric sex is the union with God through the physical union with another. Sex is a very strong force and when mixed with another's energy, it expands and it can open channels of spiritual ecstasy and communion with God. The God in each other is mixed into the experience. It takes great vulnerability to share such bliss and ecstasy. It's a form of prayer to experience the ecstasy of God with another. My higher self has told me it will be healing for me and that the next step in my spiritual growth will be to explore the sacred ecstasies of sex that will expand my energy to grow into higher states of consciousness, even other dimensions, perhaps."

"Wow! This is too much! It sounds too crazy and wonderful to be true, but I believe you. How could I not after what I saw? Ha!" he said, flirting with moving into awe and amazement, but not willing to leave all his old beliefs behind yet.

"This was my first experience of tantric sex. It was connected deeply energetically for me. That instant pleasure of following my intuitive body wisdom that was the key to open your spiritual eye, so you could see aura colors, energy colors," I explained further.

"So, you opened my third eye?" he asked, obviously not knowing much about a third eye. Yes, I've heard about the third eye."

"Well, I've heard that seeing that kind of colors with your eyes closed or auras around people, only happens when your third eye is open, your spiritual eye. So, I'm gathering that's what was happening," I explained.

"Yess! That was surprising. I don't know what to think about it. I never have given spiritual things much thought, let alone spiritual sex," he said lost in thought and obviously searching for some points of reference to what we spoke. "So I was auditioning to be your tantric sex partner and I didn't know it?" he asked amused, with a pleased twinkle in his eye at the idea.

"Yes and no," I answered. "I liked you on many levels, so I didn't approach it as the primary focus--even though it is currently a very important mission of mine."

"Well, mission accomplished," he said, looking at me playfully and busting up laughing. "Right? Tell me if what we had wasn't tantric sex. And we didn't even try."

"The whole point is not to 'try.' It's about not being in your head but in your heart and your body's intuitive feeling for a deeper energy exchange. Yes, it was a very good sign and it was tantric, but it is just the beginning," I explained.

"Well, YESSS! I will be honored to be your tantric lover," he said and I couldn't believe it was happening. I set myself out to find such a precious new piece to my spiritual growth and it was laid before my feet so effortlessly.

"I want to be your tantric lover," he said with total conviction. Then his eyes reached up to the sky lost in thought. "And so much more," he said, as if he spoke a great conclusion. "I want to be with you wholly, completely," he said and grabbed my face to look at him. "I need to ask you another very important question." I just nodded gently, my head cupped in his hands: "I'm moving to China in a week to work for one of my father's companies and I want you to move with me. I will take care of you. You can write anywhere. Come with me and we can see if we can make a life together," he said and held me close in his chest. I could feel the raw sentiment in his heartbeat and the nervousness in his deep and reaching breaths. I felt the genie of love released from where it had been bottled up in his heart floating out as vapor wanting to take form if time would allow.

I was silent.

"You're not saying anything," he insisted.

"You didn't tell me you were moving. In a week!" I said with a disappointment in my voice that began to create distance in this idyllic moment of bonding and a hesitation to the falling in love that was happening.

"Yes, but I'm asking you to come with me," he said, trying to pull us out of some manhole we had found ourselves in so soon in our journey.

"Any other time in my life I would've taken off with you, but now I just started the most amazing journey of my life with a teacher who has opened me up to spiritual experiences I can't even explain. I can't leave my classes and this guidance now," I insisted.

"I don't believe you need this teacher. You are open. You are magic."

"No, my gut tells me I absolutely need to continue with him to cultivate the opening that is happening" I said, my heart face planting in a vat of cement that was hardening quickly with loss and disappointment.

"I don't believe in the long-distance thing. It's one thing if it was back and forth from New York, but China is too far," he said.

"I agree."

"If you come with me now, we can probably come back in two years and then you can take these classes," he continued, making one last attempt to figure us out.

"No. It doesn't always work like that. I've opened to something and I have to ride the wave now," I said. "If, when you come back in two years we are both free, then we can pick up where we left off.

"Perhaps this too is a wave and if we do not ride it, it will never come back again," he said, and we both knew his words rang so true. We had to choose which wave to ride.

"I'm so disappointed. I'm so sorry this is the way it is," he said, and we just held each other for a while. We are both happy people, so we snapped out of our disappointment to have some conversation and laughs late into the evening. It already felt like we had said goodbye, so I did not want to spend the night just to have to go through it again in the morning. He drove me home.

"You know what made that armpit-elbow experience remotely possible? I just realized it was because you don't wear deodorant." We both busted up laughing.

"Ha, ha, that's true!" he said.

"I wouldn't have licked you if it had had some horrible toxic, chemical deodorant taste!" I continued.

"Yes. That was a very special experience. How will I describe this to my friends?" he said seriously, but with humor. "You didn't touch my penis. It was like an elbow blow job!" he said and we both busted up laughing.

"That's perfect, so funny. I think you'll have an interesting time explaining what an elbow blow job is."

"Now everyone is going to want an elbow blow job too!" he said and we had our final laugh together as we drove up to my house.

"Look, I know we've said what we've said and we've come to certain conclusions, but let's just think about it for a week. I hate to think something we both think is so amazing can be decided so quickly. We need to honor these special feelings. Maybe one of us will change our mind and we can go on," he suggested.

"Yes, it feels too surreal to have so much feelings so fast and then to just dismiss them so easily," I agreed.

"O.K. Then we will think and see each other in a week," he said and I nodded contented enough by the fact that we both felt the same strength of feelings even if we would not stay together.

He walked me to the door and kissed me one last time. That was one hell of a whirlwind date. We pledged our lives together and broke up all in a matter of a night!

15

"Intermission"

"The World of Energy" shall entertain you during this intermission…

End of the nineteenth century, Guatemalan Coffee Plantation in a time of tails, top hats, Victorian bustles and puffy sleeves.

The plantation house was a magnificent mansion owned by one of the wealthiest families in Guatemala. The furnishings were all from Europe. It was part of the sumptuous lifestyle that no longer exists today, "Gone with the Wind" so to speak. The plantation was called "La Florida" and was owned by my great, great grandfather from my mother's father's side of the family.

My great, great grandmother from the other side of the family, Clara, seventeen at the time, was in a spirited card game with other guests and their friends. The table started to jitter and shake.

"Earthquake! Earthquake! Everybody get out," someone yelled. All the guests sprang up, but Clara just laughed with amusement. The shaking stopped.

"Look…the chandeliers aren't moving. Nothing fell… Alejandro!" yelled the patrón, Don Luciano Monzón, my great, great grandfather.

A lanky mestizo servant came running into the room.

"Did you feel the shaking?" asked Don Luciano.

"I heard you say there was an earthquake…but we didn't feel it," Alejandro referred to the help that was working in the kitchen.

Everyone tentatively sat back down. Guatemala is one of those volcanically active countries that are terrorized by earthquakes.

"How can you just sit there and laugh, Clara? You should be more concerned when an earthquake strikes. People die," scolded the lady of the manor Don Luciano's wife, Doña Teodosia.

"It doesn't scare me. I've seen too many. And besides, everyone runs around practically wetting their pants with fear, when it's just as possible that as they try to run away from the earthquake, something could fall on them as a result of hiding in the wrong place or running this way and that way, like frantic ants. I find it funny."

"Why didn't the chandeliers move? That was the strangest earthquake," Don Luciano remarked eerily. No one seemed to have the same concern and all he got was blank faces and shrugs. He was alone in his curiosity.

"Well, let's get back to the game. The chandeliers didn't move, but the cards are a mess," Clara said as she began to scoop them up. The shaking started again. Doña Teodosia shrieked and fell back in her chair as Clara hid her laughter. Don Luciano looked up at the chandeliers.

"Look, the chandeliers are not moving!" Everyone looked up and around the parlor astounded to see that nothing else was moving: no vase, no chandelier, nothing, but the table! And the shaking stopped.

"O.K. who is doing this? Teodosia, *mi amor*, how did you fall on the floor?" said Pablo, rushing to lift her off the floor, chair and all, like a stiff doll, with the help of one of the other male guests.

"You mean someone was moving the table from underneath? It's a very heavy table," an incredulous guest scoffed as he snickered.

"It would have to be a very strong man. Are you all right Doña Teodosia? You look strained." Clara pursed her mouth to one side into a crooked frown in empathetic body language at the sight of the disheveled Doña Teodosia. Doña Teodosia straightened herself from the fall and plastered a fake smile on her face trying to cover her embarrassment, and nodded dismissively.

"Well, it was a funny prank, but enough is enough, so let's hear it...." insisted Pablo in a good-humored Spirit. "Please, bring Doña Teodosia a glass of sherry. Well?"

Everyone looked at the other and no one seemed the least bit guilty.

"O.K. Let's get back to the game. After a few more drinks someone will confess to being the clown tonight. Later, later, whoever you are; you must confess," Don Luciano playfully prodded.

They played peacefully for a while. Then the strange quaking began again!

Everyone raced to look under the table. But no one was touching the table from below. It moved on its own. This time Clara didn't even laugh. There was a silence among them. And Doña Teodosia started to whimper.

"Oh, darling. At least it's not an earthquake," consoled Don Luciano.

"No, it's a ghost or worse! One of these Indians has cursed us."

"Why don't you retire, dear? I think your nerves have had it."

"Nooooh." She sounded like a ghost herself. "I don't want to be alone."

"Then calm yourself. Another sherry for Teodosia."

"Maybe the sherry is not a good idea. She's getting very emotional," warned Clara.

"Drunk is the word. I'm hoping it will knock her out since the fall of the chair didn't," Pablo whispered to Clara making her laugh out loud "inappropriately" again.

"You know, I saw a gypsy show in France where the magician could make a table move. He allowed anyone to come up close to inspect and no one could figure out how he did it," one of the young gentlemen, Don Carlitos, shared.

"So, one of us has magic powers?" another of the guests mocked.

"Yes! That's it! It only happens when we play cards. Haven't you noticed?" Don Luciano exclaimed to a wall of muttering confirmations and nods.

"And if I were to guess, the person doesn't even know that they are doing it," chimed in Don Carlitos.

"Yes. I saw everyone's face and no one seemed to be faking their concern or lack of it," Clara pointed to herself: "I'm good at reading faces."

"A test!" Don Luciano said conspiratorially.

"This will be a more interesting game than cards," said Clara.

They all took their seats around the table and one by one, individually, put their hands on the table. They would each get a minute. You could cut the anticipation with a knife. Don Carlitos was first–nothing.

Doña Teodosia's hands were quivering from all the sherry, but the table didn't budge. Don Luciano placed his hands on the table.

"Come on. Come on. I want to believe in this magic. Come on…" His minute was up–nothing! He pounded the table in disappointment and everyone laughed, relieving the tension.

"Are we going to burn the witch at the stake when we find out who it is? That's what they do to witches, isn't it?" Clara joked as she laid her hands on the table.

"You don't see us burning all these Indians and they do all kinds of spells and witchcraft, don't they?" replied Doña Teodosia.

"I was just teasing. There are no such things…" Clara stopped midsentence.

The table rumbled, silencing the room.

"…I'm the witch?" Clara gasped.

"Clara!" Don Luciano exclaimed in utter amazement.

The table shook violently!

"*Dios Mío*! What is it?" Doña Teodosia swayed, tipsy in her seat.

"I'm not a witch! I didn't do anything." Clara retracted her hands stunned.

The room was silent. A few of the guests looked at Clara with a little fear. Then everyone erupted in laughter. Clara studied her hands as if she expected to see boils or burns; some sign of lurid energies at work. They looked normal.

"We know you're not a witch. And this never happened, before?" asked Don Luciano.

"No. Never. I'm as surprised as you are."

"Fascinating! Put your hands on, again and leave them on the table. Don't take them off," Carlitos insisted.

Clara put her hands back on the table and the rumbling grew to shaking again. Then the table literally started to jump up and down...until it appeared to be walking.

Petite, lithe Clara was able to move the table that would usually take 4 men to carry across the floor! That night she had birthed some kind of kinetic energy that flowed through her hands completely unconsciously!

Clara started to play with her ability over time and discovered that she could move other huge wood objects by just resting her hands on them and they would start to jump and walk across the floor at her will. If the object had too much metal it wouldn't respond to her touch as easily. It became a type of parlor trick to entertain her friends, and that was all. She could move huge armoires that would take 6 men to lift. As she got older she would breakdown crying after doing a demonstration of her strange ability. Some say the energy was too much for her as she got older and others say that it scared her a bit, because she didn't understand it.

Why did Clara's ability to energetically move large wood objects kick in suddenly? She never had a hint of activity slowly building to this display of energy theatrics. And how was it that she didn't even feel anything that would lead her to know it was she who was channeling this energy that moved the table? There are so many questions when it comes to understanding our body and the world in regards to energy.

If it had been in the current time, perhaps it would have been encouraged and accepted for her to focus her ability for healing. She obviously had an unusual energy that flowed through her that allowed her to do unexplainable things. Perhaps she would have been able to help people open their energy channels like Thad, for she was born with the gift of being able to "move energy" through and out of her body.

Thad mentioned once that he thought that the ability to conduct an opening to deeper energy may partially be due to genetics. Maybe I inherited my ability to open up my energy channels from Clara, my great grandmother. Maybe when my ability is fully developed, I'll have a future as a healer...or a furniture mover. Ha!

* * *

I read a fascinating book called "The Heart Code" by Paul Pearsall, a psycho-neuro-immunologist, who interviewed many heart transplant patients and documented many stories that led him to believe that memory must somehow be encoded in the cells of the heart and perhaps the whole body. In these various interviews the heart recipient would give accounts of new emotions and feelings that seemed to be altered by the temperament of the donor. Some recipients had detailed dreams as to how the donor died.

There was one such case where an older gentleman said that he had giddy feelings of love and hope and lightness that he had never had. He also kept having nightmares of a young girl that was killed when she was hit by a car. When Dr. Pearsall interviewed the donor family, about whom the recipient had not any previous information, he learned that the donor was a very young, energetic, optimistic woman who was about to be married and her heart was full of love and promise for her future. It was confirmed that she had died when being struck by a car.

There were other cases where the families of the donor recipient said that the temperament, interests and even food preferences changed after the transplant. One man couldn't stomach food spiced with chili and after his transplant he loved hot, spicy food. Again, when Dr. Pearsall tracked down the donor's family the change in temperament and personality matched that of the donor.

Dr. Pearsall states that the heart, not the brain, sends out the strongest magnetic field of the whole body. Perhaps my desire after all these energy openings to let my heart lead more than my intellect is simply reconnecting to natural instinct.

There is a non-profit organization that has studied the heart-brain connection since 1991 called HeartMath. It has found through research that the heart influences the brain as much or more than the brain influences the body and heart. The heart seems to be a little command post that has its own functional "brain" that sends messages to the cranial brain, profoundly affecting performance and function of most of the body's major organs and ultimately determining the quality of life. So far, they have been able to identify four ways in which the heart communicates with the brain: neurologically (nervous system), biophysically (pulse wave), biochemically (hormones), energetically (electromagnetic fields).

Did you know that the heart is not just a muscle, but it is also a hormonal gland? In 1983 it was discovered that the heart secreted hormones and thus was reclassified. The heart synthesizes and releases neurotransmitters, norepinephrine and dopamine, once thought to be produced only by neurons in the brain and ganglia outside the heart. The heart produces just as much oxytocin, the "love" or "bonding hormone" as the brain!

HeartMath has developed techniques that bring calm and centeredness to the heart brain and then help the brain sync up to the heart's state, entraining the whole body to work in greater harmony. When a constructive synergy of the intelligence of both mind and heart is bridged, it profoundly heightens perception, awareness, and intelligence.

"Since emotional processes can work faster than the mind, it takes a power stronger than the mind to bend perception, override emotional circuitry and provide us with intuitive feeling instead. It takes the power of the heart"

- Doc Childre
Founder of The Institute of HeartMath

We are a complex system of layered energies that we are still learning how to unleash, synchronize, focus and harness for optimum experience of what it is to be human. We seem to be a mass of energy imprints buried in our nervous system and cells. And these cells seem to be able to send energy imprints and messages not just within our body, but out into the natural world and to communicate with the cellular memory of others.

I woke up one morning, many years ago, starving. I went to the kitchen and made myself a huge bowl of oatmeal. Just when I was about to eat, I felt weary and dopy, as if I had been drugged. So, I went to my bed, put the oatmeal on the night table, and fell into a comatose sleep.

I dreamt I was going up an escalator in the airport. In front of me was a young couple and the female was pulling a wheeled hot plate that had a few eggs frying sunny side up.

"Why are you frying eggs?" I asked.

"They're my eggs from my ovaries and I'm cooking them to make a baby."

We got to the top of the escalator and there was an older woman waiting for them. "I'm not strong enough to carry the baby so we're implanting it into my aunt."

"Wow! Science is so amazing!" I exclaimed in total awe as I watched them pick up the eggs and drop them into a clear bag of water, like they do at the pet shop when you buy a goldfish.

...I awoke in a twilight sleep as I turned to sleep on my other side. I opened my eyes and saw my room. I felt like I was just above my body and I was in a pillowy, pleasurable, euphoric feeling. It all felt soooo good. I went right back to my dream where I left off...

The frying eggs instantly turned into these little sea creature, humanoids, similar to those I remember seeing in comic books called "Sea Monkeys" that you could order and they would grow out of little granules into sea people-like creatures that you could keep in your aquarium.

It's so amazing what science can do now...it's so amazing what science can do!" I said like Dorothy's mantra: "There's no place like home," when she clicked her heels and woke up in her bed.

I woke up and went immediately to share the remarkable, funny dream with my mother. I started to recount the events in my dream when my mother busted out," Oh my god!"

"What? What is it?" I asked confused by her reaction.

"Just keep going. I'll tell you in a minute."

I finished recounting my dream about the amazing blissful feeling as I slept.

"Now, I'm going to tell you something," my mom started. "I've been so worried whether I should tell you or not, yet. I haven't been able to sleep well this week and have been debating with your aunt if we should tell you until she's made up her mind for sure. Your aunt wants to have another child. The doctor says that she is healthy enough to carry the baby, even at her age, but her eggs are too old. She was thinking of asking you to donate some of your eggs. But we, especially me, have been worried of the implications and the confusing feelings that this could create for you. Would you feel it's your child? It would be your child and your cousin...How would you feel about it?"

"Of course I would do it. I don't have any problem at all. I wouldn't see it as my child. It would be my cousin," I answered resolutely, matter-of-factly.

"I can't believe you dreamt it. I can't tell you the instant relief it has given me. I couldn't sleep last night."

My mother and I dream of the other when we're in trouble or very stressed about something. When as a teenager I was deathly ill and home alone, because my parents were traveling in Europe, she said she had bad dreams about me all the time and felt that I needed her. I didn't let on that I was ill, because I didn't want to spoil their trip.

Energy moves in instantaneous pathways that are still of great mystery. One thing I know is that we can synchronize and communicate through the heart, through our cells, not only from a few feet away or when we are in the close presence of another human being, as the studies from the Heart-Math group say, but we can send and receive messages instantaneously, regardless of distance. There is a connection that goes beyond time and space. Science has seen this type of unified (instantaneous) resonance connectivity between particles in experiments that have to do with quantum entanglement and quantum teleportation.

Quantum entanglement refers to particles that were once entangled together, but then when separated, regardless of the distance between them, know instantly the state of the other particle. The two particles, or photons, always know the state of the former entangled partner. In this way, you tap a Morse code or spin one particle and the other particle, regardless of distance, will be altered in the same way. This opens up the possibilities in the field of quantum teleportation. This is not teleportation as seen in Star Trek movies, but it is a way that information can be sent instantaneously. Scientists don't understand what it is that connects the particles and it is obviously beyond the speed of light restrictions, but they know it works, nonetheless.

Perhaps it is because we were once entangled with the "All" of creation, whether seen from the scientific theory of the "Big Bang," or the spiritual belief that we are one in the spirit of God, the Conscious Life Force Energy. It all points to the possibility that we are ultimately connected and inseparable and can communicate on an energetic level, making us ultimately telepathic if we open our channels.

I was lying on the floor in Thad's yoga class in between poses when the simple act of Thad walking past me and doing the double yogic breath set my kundalini off and opened me to a deep intuitive state. I leapt into a backbend and started to shake my head back and forth. From then on, whenever Thad approached me or took a deep breath close to me, it would set me off energetically. I noticed this happened to others in the class as well. During our sessions it was the same. Just lying on the table would alter my breath, my body temperature would rise, and I would intuitively contort into positions that my body required in that specific moment to release tension into bliss.

There is so much emotional and physical tension that seems to need to be shaken out to release trapped energies. It seems to me that this kind of shaking off of the tension is something that heals past wounds and needs to be done on a regular basis to keep tensions and emotions from accumulating and shutting us down in the present.

One cannot chuck the response I, and others, have had to Thad as a Pavlov's response. I see it as a process of me becoming more sensitive to energy as my channels opened, for when I've gone through periods of not cultivating my practice of meditation, clean diet, bodywork, yoga, and "good company" (those that are truly trustworthy to share my most tender, soft, joyous self) the channels have closed and I have not entered as easily into these ecstatic, deeper, energy-sensitive states anymore. And when these channels closed, I would not be as affected by Thad's energy in yoga class. Getting too intimate with those that were overly negative, dismissive, manipulative or dishonest definitely caused the openings to diminish in frequency and depth.

The Thad phenomenon seems to be more of a tuning fork mechanism at work, wherein he seems to have a strong field that encourages others to resonate with his energy. And, likewise, those that can more easily resonate with the energies of others--such as empaths--can probably be more energetically moved by Thad. Perhaps there is some kind of merging of energy or "energy entanglement" that is the result of an "ability" that Thad has that creates this energetic connection.

I remember I was five to six months out of a relationship with someone that was one of the loves of my life when I started to think about him all the time and felt sad. I had broken up with him and I had moved on to another relationship and never gave him much thought until that one week.

Happenstance would have it that one of my best friends ran into my ex-lover at a bank. She said that he looked very sad and wanted to know what I was up to and said that he'd like to hear from me before he went to Germany on vacation. I never called him and after another week of the sadness and thoughts of him on the forefront of my mind, the feeling went as suddenly as it had come. I think we had gotten so close, that the connection was still there and I could feel his sadness over the loss of our relationship that sprung up in him. Once he went off to Germany and stopped thinking about me, I stopped feeling him.

It wasn't my sadness I was feeling. It was his. It's a whole other art and level of awareness to learn when feelings are one's own and when they are empathic or sympathetic.

So, just like science can't explain how many things work, I can't explain scientifically either how my energetic awakening worked, but I can explain what I sense, feel, and the images I get that give me understanding in a metaphoric way. And I only know "IT" is real by seeing the results and changes that let me know "IT" works: "IT," the Conscious Life Force Energy.

Since my energetic awakening, I feel that my energy speeds up, as if I am resonating at a higher vibration and communication becomes more fluid in all regards: within my psyche from conscious to subconscious and from one person to another, throughout my body. Everything flows and fires quicker. Just as ice melts into water and water evaporates and lifts into the atmosphere to form a cloud, our energy--through the kundalini heat awakening—can change our own energy into a form that moves through the world in quicker, instantaneous ways or transmutes it completely, bringing deeper connection and eventually total "communion" with all and freedom from past wounding.

It's like I resonate with a frequency that correlates with a state of mind that opens up a new world of possibilities of moving energy. Perhaps a connection with this dimension can help further understand the unified theory and how we may be able to travel beyond the speed of light. The instantaneous energy shifts I have experienced seem to be bringing that understanding of the unified field into a firsthand plausibility. But like the scientist not knowing exactly how it works, I know it works because I see the effect in my mind and body; but I can't see the force, just as gravity can't be seen, but we experience its effects.

Stories of old speak of spiritually advanced beings that can perform what we call "miracles" in the West, "siddhis" (supernatural powers in Hindi faith), such as appearing in several places simultaneously, or transporting themselves someplace in an instance, telepathy, healing through touch or transforming one object into another. All of these speak to the truths scientists prescribe as possible in the quantum world. It's wonderful that science is able to begin to support these theories in the laboratory. Teleportation of particles is in its infancy. Scientists have bent space/time in the laboratory and believe that Black Holes are tears in the space/time fabric, discoveries that bring us closer to time travel through scientific means.

It's strange that "science" is held in earnest and considered to be in its right mind when teaching the theories of the quantum world, but when the exact same possibilities are spoken of as a result of developed or inherited abilities of those spiritual aspirants who have cultivated their energy/body, it is considered quackery.

As I remember the spiritual tales of miracles and my experience of new capabilities and peek experiences through my awakening to "The Life Force Energy," I believe we cannot exclude cultivating our body, mind, and soul as instruments of quantum capability. Maybe we'll be able to induce these quantum realm truths through mechanical means, but perhaps we are the ultimate quantum machine as we learn to switch on our as of yet dormant "enlightenment genes" in our DNA.

"Energy is the force that moves things, including atoms, molecules, cellular processes, consciousness, and bodies from planets to toes. It moves systems because it contains the information that tells systems how to move. Measuring energy has become a very precise science, but interpreting what energy actually is challenges even the most brilliant physicists. There is great difficulty in understanding the true nature of energy and how an invisible process can contain information that affects every system in the cosmos…gravity holds you in a chair, but you can't see or touch it. We know and feel the effects of electromagnetic energy, but we can only see it in its indirect manifestations accessible to our physical sense.

"The possibility of a new type of force should not be ruled out because of our inability to directly measure it with our current instruments or to understand the nature of its encoded information."

Paul Pearsall
"The Heart's Code"

There is a conscious energy that is the bonding brain force of the universe. It is invisible, unless you learn to use your other heightened senses as telescopic eyes that can feel and merge into the world of the quantum realm of infinite possibilities and into communion with the Life Force Energy, that may be the unifying force in the universe Einstein believed existed.

The influences, the layers that conjoin to create each of us as individuals are many: from traumas and memories in this current life lodged in our body, or the genetic memories of our ancestors: like, perhaps, my inheriting my great grandmother's Clara's sensitivity to energy, or the cellular memory from a heart transplant donor, to tapping into the memory of the collective unconscious of all of humanity throughout history, to the energy imprint in our mysterious "Junk DNA," where abilities may lie that determine the evolutionary trajectory of our human species. We seem to be a starburst of energy confluences. Each ray of the starburst pertains to a layer of our being and intersecting these layers creates prisms, patterns of thought and feeling that channel or regulate our energetic ability and awareness.

As I opened my energy channels, I was beginning to perceive the world as a fabric of energy that connects us all. The energy channels were growing like tentacles in every direction like an energy tree. The roots were growing deeper into an energetic connection to my primordial and ancestral lineage, the branches parallel to the earth, constantly integrating and relating to the present, all while the tree top was winding up to the heavens, pulling in understanding of the energetic possibilities of the future. I felt like an Energy Starburst Tree.

Intermission Has Ended – Back to the Quest for Tantric Sex…

16

"Lust Makes the Spirit Willing"

"Suraya, will you please come and switch partners with Sarah? I want you to work with Dillion," Thad instructed. Dillion was one of only two men in the training course and after several classes of having people work on him, he wasn't "moving energy." He wasn't feeling the energy open up in his body into vulnerability or ecstasy.

I dutifully shuffled across the floor to change partners.

"I want to do an experiment," Thad proclaimed. "It's my hunch that if Suraya works on Dillion he will open up."

The whole class was stopped to watch me work on Dillion and apply the new techniques and work on some new "high charge points," the acupuncture points that help one open up to the unconscious holding patterns of energy.

Dillion was one of the youngest in the class, twenty, golden blond hair down to his shoulders and a very nice body. A Nordic-looking Tarzan would describe him. As I went to work on Dillion the Kundalini energy started to open in my body as had become customary throughout this training.

I worked on Dillion's *erector spinae*, the muscle that runs up and down his spine, and he started to giggle. I kept working and the heat started to open in his body. He started to writhe on the table and then suddenly he was growling like a lion. He jumped up on the table and was roaring and screaming. Everyone laughed. He was contorting, quivering and sweating with the release of energy circulating through his body.

"See? The opposite, polar energies work best: male and female—unless you're gay or really open to allowing yourself to feel pleasure from the same sex. The sexual arousal helps open up the energy. I had a hunch he would find that chemistry with Suraya and that would help him open up to the work," Thad exclaimed.

Some people may hear this and think it sounds slightly inappropriate, but it couldn't be further from the truth. It's about not being afraid of the sensual, sexual arousal and riding the wave of energy to open you up to your own deeper self: repressed emotions or ecstasies of your own Life Force Energy that are bound in your unconscious. It has nothing to do with feeling desire for the body worker or client or any kind of sexual objectification.

I never felt like I was special or had some new power that allowed me to help others open up their energy in the class. Energy was awakened in me and now it seemed that I, too, could assist in awakening the movement of energy in others. I really feel that although I seemed to have a specific effect on Dillion, one could not ignore the fact that Thad's presence in the room was part of the ingredient that produced the outcome. I felt his mere presence connected me to my free-flowing energy, which put me in a state where I in turn was effective in facilitating energy to move in others. I am not so sure I would be as effective outside of class and outside of Thad's presence.

17

"Ride the Wave"

Something more was changing in my being. I could've been thought-burdened by the choice to go away with someone that apparently had the makings of an amazing tantric lover and maybe even a love relationship as Wolfgang hinted at being, but because of the fullness of my inner experience I just couldn't think about it in a way that evoked pain of loss. I was too much in the moment with everything that was going on as my inner transformation continued to unfold. I was drawn to be with him more than I had been pulled by anyone in years, so I did think about my spiritual path and my love life and the way they could possibly combine between China and Los Angeles. After all, I had traveled back and forth to India seven times in two years and survived, so why not China?

"Hello beautiful," Wolfgang said as I answered the phone.

"Hi my lumpkin," I said teasing, smiling at the sound of his voice.

"I just wanted to say that I can't wait to see you" Wolfgang said, stirring up the pull to be with him and the power between us.

"Me too," I said wistfully, feeling the floor and my heart had moving parts that I hadn't put together just yet.

"But there is a problem. I can't see you," he said with a strange sound in his voice that I couldn't put my finger on.

"Why? What happened?" I said shocked, feeling my anticipation fall flat.

"Because I can't see through walls," he said and my heart jumped, for that meant he was outside my house. I was in some mismatched baggy sweats so I jumped up to change not wanting to be caught looking like an unkempt hobo. Luckily, my face and hair were put together.

I answered the door and Wolfgang reached out for my hand. I put my hand in his and he pulled me into a kiss.

"What made you drop by without notice? What if I weren't here?" I asked.

"If you weren't here, I would wait for you," he said. "I was driving home calling you to make plans for our big talk and I was literally passing by your house, so I veered up to see if I could catch you and give you a personal invitation."

"O.K. Well, you got me."

"I was going to invite you to dinner or lunch, but I'm a sunset aficionado so I thought this would be the perfect time. Is today a good day for me to whisk you away or do you prefer tomorrow?" he asked.

"I'm a sunset aficionado too! That's exactly what I tell people. Ha!" I said, truly surprised at the coincidence. "Let's go, take me where you shall!" and we started laughing as we so easily did.

We didn't drive far to the bluffs that overlook the ocean and the Santa Monica and Malibu coastline.

"I've been thinking about the situation. I want to be with you too. Why don't you stay here? Don't go," I said to his surprise.

"Ah, it didn't occur to me that you would ask that of me," he said and laughed surprised. "I guess it would be the gallant and romantic thing to do," he contemplated.

"How could that option not occur to you?" I asked.

"Because it is about money. How else could I support you, us, if I don't make a good living," he said.

"Can't you continue to do what you've been doing for your dad's company here?" I inquired.

"My father is not easy. I've had to work for everything with him. Sending me to China is a promotion. He has already hired someone to take my place here, anyway. I would cause so much upheaval with a change of heart. I would have to give everyone much advanced notice. If I were to do that, I would have to give him like six months to make adjustments. So, you see it would be better if you follow me because I'm the one who has to take care of us."

"For you it's about money, for me it's about my soul. My soul is opening and speaking to me about ecstasy and freeing me of burdensome thoughts that keep me from the deeper love of life and living. My worth in this existence is tied to that understanding. The wave I must ride is here with this new teacher and his teachings. This time is a moment of destiny for me. To meet such a destiny as I'm experiencing is the gift of all gifts. The kundalini is the fountain of miracles that is teaching me and it is best nurtured here."

Wolfgang was silent and just nodded and pulled me into a full embrace.

"I can't argue with that. If I ever felt that way, it would be worth more than the millions I will make. I understand," Wolfgang said.

"You started to see aura colors when we were having sex. It was opening your third eye. Did that not move you to want to open up more?"

"I saw some colors and I loved the strange new pleasures I felt in my body, in my armpit of all places and my elbow, who would've thought, but that's not enough to have me give up this opportunity. It made me want to be with you more than follow some spiritual thing."

"It's not the colors. It's what's behind them," I interjected. "The understanding of who we are and how that will change the way we create, move and even love in this world. Now that I feel this opening it has given me new hope as to what we may evolve to be in the future. It's so magnificent. I hope my hope is true" I explained, with an idealistic passion I had not realized I had forgotten through the years.

Wolfgang was staring at me deeply the whole time I spoke. It was as if he was taking in more than the words. He was taking in my inspiration. He felt the hope was real to me and it became real to him.

"Yes, I would like to continue this exploration if it holds such promise," he said smiling at me in a kind of sweet gratitude. "But I will have to continue it in China. Perhaps I will find a teacher there," he said. "It's so nice to hear such innocent words from a woman. I have not heard such deep words in a long time, maybe ever," he said and laughed. "Such a shame."

Darkness had befallen our sunset view and we headed back to my house.

"Can I come in for one last time?" Wolfgang asked with a hint of pain in the tone of his voice.

"No, I don't want to be so intimate knowing it's the end," I replied

"Ok. How about for just one last time to do that thing you did to my arm? I want to see if it happens again," he said appealing to my sense of exploration to try to be close anyway he could.

"You mean the elbow blow job?" I said.

"Yes! Yes! The elbow blow job!" he said and we busted up laughing."

"Yes, I guess it would be interesting to give it another try," I agreed with a resurgence to get in the game with him again for the sake of curiosity.

We went to the bedroom and stripped down in a minute.

"No deodorant?" I asked.

"No deodorant," he answered raising a "come hither" eyebrow.

"Oh, you came prepared," I said laughing.

"Can you blame me?" he said and leapt on the bed.

We kissed deeply wrapped in each other's arms. Then without speaking I tied his right arm and both legs to the bedposts. I started to fellate his arm, diving into his armpits, trailing down the inside of his biceps to devour his elbow. He moaned and squirmed as best as a man tied up could squirm.

"Are you seeing colors?"

"No, but I'm so turned on, I'm on the edge."

I stopped tending to his arm to kiss him deep, long. As we kissed I untied his arm. He began caressing my body fast and furiously anywhere, anyhow he could grab and rub and prod me. Then I lunged back into his armpit and bit especially viciously.

"Ohhh!" He cried out. "I'm in a blast of colors. I can see them with my eyes open now. They're dancing around you."

I bit down his arm to his elbow.

"Ouch!" He exclaimed as I bit his elbow bone hard. "Ah, ah, ohhh!! I'm coming!" He said as he climaxed. I sat up and stared at him smiling and laughing.

"That was so amazing. It was stronger than last time. It's crazy," he exclaimed.

"Dude, I don't know. This comes too easy to you. Maybe this isn't me but is just some weird thing about you?" I said skeptically as I quickly untied his legs.

"I don't know, but I love you! I love this! And this has never happened before," he said catching his breath and he pulled me into his arms and into a kiss as he still wound down.

We lay naked in the dark, into the silent night where we heard nothing but our own chatter and the nightingale that sings so energetically in the summer months. I wondered what the nightingales were saying to each other. Were they too discussing love and their future or just the joys of the summer night's breeze and the plump earthworms they had feasted on that night. The more the night settled into darkness, I could feel our time stretch thin until it was gone.

"Even though we have just begun and we won't be seeing each other anymore, I want to tell you...that I love you. Not like the 'I love you' everyone says around here that means nothing, a vague friendship. I'm in love with you," he said with a sincerity that covered me with such sentiment of love, that I could feel my vulnerable self and without filter or hesitation I had the courage to speak of the tender shy feelings that usually takes time to confess.

"You are my love too," I said with a love welling up that did not belong to the brief encounter we had.

"It was love at first sight for me," he said.

"No, not at first sight..." I said flirtatiously..."love at first cold spoon," I joked and he chuckled.

"Love at first cold fork," he said joining in the joke and we busted up laughing as our horizon stretched to an end.

18
"The Smell of Death Still on His Breath"

"**Y**ou know, he got married again since you've seen him and this last wife died of a drug overdose just a year into the marriage." The Guru Agent, now my Tantric Matchmaker, informed me about the next date he wanted to set me up with.

"I've always said that I'll never date a widower. It wasn't his choice to leave the person they have lost; she has been ripped out of his life and then the person who comes afterwards into his life can never live up to the idealized memory that is created of the deceased spouse. I think we should cancel," I said.

"No, no...it's nothing like that. It's already been a while, like a year ago, and he wasn't happy at all. In fact, two weeks before she died he said he was going to divorce her. They got married in a whirlwind romance and she started to do drugs with his daughter and they started to fight all the time. They stopped going out socially due to their angst and he is a really social guy. Don't worry. He's probably relieved the relationship is over," the Guru Agent reassured.

"OK. Book it! We're on for Friday," I agreed.

* * *

The widower answered the door to his posh Beverly Hills home. He had a real happy glint in his eye upon seeing me. Maybe he was over the death of his ex-wife. He was giddy, flirtatious and full of humorous quips, just as I had remembered him from years ago before the divorce from his first wife and the death of his second wife.

He invited me in and we sat on the couch to reacquaint ourselves. Very early on, mid-conversation about his businesses and his movie projects I got a very odd feeling that he was not telling me the whole truth about what he did for a living. I got an uncomfortable feeling about him. A very clear voice in my head said: " He's a sleazy producer. He is a sneaky liar. He isn't honest about what he does." It was so strong I couldn't help but blurt out my feelings trying to downplay the chilling concern it was giving me.

"You know, I get this feeling that you're sneaky: a sleazy producer. I've never gotten this hit about anyone before," I started.

He looked astounded, but found it so humorous he was reeling with laughter, I suppose at my gall in being so blunt.

"Sleazy? Nooo way! Sneaky? Sneaky good. Like I like to surprise people with presents." He smiled slyly through his laughter. "You know, I love to give jewelry."

"No. Sneaky bad. Like you're a sleazy producer," I said in disbelief that I found myself insulting the date I was really enjoying; but he seemed to find it so entertaining that it encouraged my honesty. "Like you're not telling me the truth about something about what you do for work," I continued.

"No, no...I'm telling you the truth. There's nothing to worry about. I just make a few pies and cakes in my dessert company and I'm trying to get a few movies made. Oh, and I have a medical device/supply company." He just kept laughing as if he found his answer just as amusing. "Why don't we head on into dinner?"

I don't usually get such specific intuitive hits on people. And after all, how did I know it was not my own insecurity trying to find reasons not to get close to someone. After all, it takes time to know someone. Right? I had only run into him at meditations and ashrams half way around the world. He must be a good guy, a man of integrity to have such a strong spiritual path.

The dining room table was beautifully set for two and he served me the meal his cook had prepared for us. He was so sweet and attentive throughout dinner. We had a million things we could talk about since we had many common interests. He had been an acupuncturist, a macrobiotic cook, a writer, and was now a movie producer and a businessman. We just chatted and laughed the night away.

"So where is your daughter? How old is she?" I asked, as we moved back to the couch where I had originally grilled him about being sneaky and sleazy. I had never dated anyone with a kid, let alone a teenager. I'm sure "The Silver Fat Fox" had kids, but he didn't mention them.

"Elle is sixteen and she's away at camp. She won't be back for another month," he sighed.

"Well, that sounds like fun. What kind of camp? What kind of activities do they do?" I inquired.

"Oh...it's in Colorado...um...you know horseback riding, nature survival courses and I'm sure they do all that outdoorsy stuff...um the usual...campy stuff."

"That's so cool. I love all that stuff. I love outdoorsy stuff. I am really into hiking and I love horses."

"Yeah, me, too," he said laughing as if it was funny that we had so much in common.

"I also am into meditating, as you know…"

"Hell, we met in India, of course I know," he said mockingly.

"Have you ever open-eye meditated?" I asked. "I'd like to do that with you."

"No. What do we do?"

"The intent is to connect at the soul level with another. It's a practice intended to teach you to recognize the soul first, that which is the common denominator that unifies us all. The practice puts to task the saying "The eyes are the window to the soul." It is the breath that you ride into the eyes and soul of your partner in this exercise. Your partner often becomes like a mirror to see into your own self and state of mind," I explained. "Sit close, Indian style, and face me. Take long deep breaths like you're trying to breathe me in and merge with me."

The kundalini was in such an awakened state in me, it opened immediately and I was in a very loving place and the heat kicked in. He was a natural and had a total openness towards me and the experience. He gazed so lovingly at me. Then tears welded up in his eyes.

"I didn't think I'd feel this way again so soon," he said.

"Feel what?" I asked.

"Love. I didn't think I'd fall in love like this so soon since the death of my wife."

It had been a year so I felt it was perhaps a good time for him to start to open again. We continued to share these intense feelings and attraction just through our eyes for about thirty minutes.

"So how do we do this? Do we date for a while, first?" he asked.

"Yeah. I think that's a good idea," I replied. He pulled me onto his lap so that I was straddling him and kissed me. We forgot ourselves in an endless kiss as we made-out for a while. The spark had turned into a blaze. Then I came out of the fiery state of rapture between us enough to notice it was four in the morning! These tantric lover interviews are long dates!

"What sign are you?" I asked.

"I'm a Scorpio. You know what they say about Scorpios?" He smiled.

"Yeah, yeah. They're supposed to be very sexual. I don't know much about Scorpios. Are they sneaky?" I winked.

"Ha, ha, ha…Sneaky good. When do I get to see you next? Tomorrow?"

19

"Love and Lust"

I was at my friend's trendy clothing store in Brentwood for a little girlie gossip.

"So, you're not going to believe what a fun adventure I'm on," I prompted the girls behind the counter.

"Tell us. We're dying to hear," La Bellina said in her ever-cute Latina accent.

"Well, I'm having friends set me up with men to try to find a tantric lover for me."

"No! How funny! And how has it been going? Do tell." La Bellina leaned forward and swung her long black hair behind her back in one gesture as she settled in for the intrigue. She is a Venezuelan temptress who has had many escapades in her dating life as well. In fact, she says that she cares nothing about a career, but finding her man is her career.

"So far I've gone out with three guys and they were all great dates that lasted late into the early morning. I can't tell you what a kick it is to go out with someone when that motive of finding "a tantric lover" is on the table. There is such a charge in the air. But oddly enough, it has almost had the opposite effect I thought it would."

"So how was the tantric sex?" La Bellina giggled.

"One was really promising, but he was moving to China! The others, I just kissed. I'm still in the selection process. I've got to get to know them a bit more and like them as people too. It's not as scandalous as it may sound. So, I'm still on the tantric lover hunt."

"Yes. If you sleep with a guy too soon he won't take you seriously," Camille, the other sales' girl, chimed in. "You've got to date for a few months, first. They can think you're easy. But guys don't fall in love until they have sex. They just can't think that you're too easy. It's all in that book *The Rules*." She was obviously misunderstanding something. Camille was a blond with delicate features and a slender tan body that would make her a waspy poster child of the California Blond.

"Well, actually it worked the complete opposite of *The Rules*," I said.

"Really?" Camille said, realizing she had missed some beats of the story.

"They seemed to imply that they fell in love with me on the first date. They all wanted to sweep me off my feet in some manner or another.

I've never had such a response from men. I put it on the table that I was seeking tantric sex and that I didn't want a committed relationship at first," I explained.

"Oh!" Camille stood corrected and looking confused.

"Well, look at that. How funny. It was like reverse psychology or something. Maybe I should tell my dates I'm looking for a tantric lover and that I don't care about a relationship," La Bellina giggled, again.

"But I did say that it could lead to a relationship," I explained. "I just wanted full honesty of emotions. I could fall madly in love, and so could they, but first we were to explore the tantric sex. I've never read that book *The Rules*, by the way."

"Me neither. I make my own rules," said La Bellina as she rolled her eyes and giggled. "But I don't think this would happen to just anyone. I'm telling you, and I get way more men than most women. I know very beautiful girls, gorgeous," she pointed discretely with her eyes at Camille, "who get less dates than you and I do. We have something. Maybe, it's our Latina appeal" reasoned La Bellina, who has passed for Ms. Venezuela at red carpet events.

"I'm telling you" I said, "It's never been like this. Something is different. Maybe they're so turned on by the proposition that they think I'm going to be the kinkiest sex monkey swinging from the chandeliers. So they think they've found their ideal woman," I pondered with these felines whose dating savvy was on a par with the intellectual *tête-a-tête* of the supposed venerable geniuses at the Rand Corporation when speaking on world affairs.

"Well, did you never rebel and this is like…your time to free yourself and go crazy and sleep around?" said the other sales girl, Tamara, with a sly smile. "Do you come from a repressed background and you're finally throwing off the constraints of your upbringing? Were you Catholic? I went to a Catholic girls' school and that makes you hornier." Tamara was another blond with an international twist to her ethnic roots so that one couldn't pinpoint her origins. "This sounds like a great story for once. I'm tired of these girls that read *The Rules* and are so boring," she pointed with her eyes at Camille, just as La Bellina had done before. "What girl doesn't want a good tantric sex partner or two, right? What the hell does it mean, anyway?"

La Bellina practically spit up her food laughing and came to my defense.

"I know Suraya and she's not repressed, not one bit. She's not crazy either, running around with just anybody. And I agree with her that there are no rules when it comes to love. You can meet someone and sleep with him quickly and it can turn into the best relationship or you can date someone for a while and then when you finally have sex, he changes and it doesn't work out," La Bellina spoke out emphatically.

"I'm not saying she has to be a super slut to make the story interesting," Tamara quipped and everyone laughed. "But what am I saying? The story is already crazy enough. Go on..."

"Tell them about the kundalini and all the energy... explain to them about your sacred sex and new type of orgasms," La Bellina said egging on their curiosity and somehow inferring that I was a colorful, entertaining, lunatic. She giggled. "It's actually all very interesting... hee, hee, hee."

"Well, one thing that is different is that my continuous energy openings have changed the way I see sexual allowance and actually have made me more selective and discriminating. I can't be with anyone just because he is attractive, intelligent and makes me laugh. He will have to be open to sex as a means to acquire greater awareness of self," I explained.

"Well, a guy is going to say yes to anything if it has to do with sex," La Bellina said.

"Yeah, they're gonna come to you and say they need your sex to heal them...hee, hee, hee," Tamara agreed.

"That's true. It won't be easy to find the real deal," I said. "I just have to go along with the quest and see what I find."

"And Tamara, I'm not motivated from a moralistic standpoint, but from a level of responsibility to my own growth. To cultivate this growing awareness of energy I have to choose clear, positive, trustworthy, truly loving individuals as partners that can handle the depth and vulnerability that the process of opening up to my deeper self is taking me on. I have to trust the person with whom I'm going to possibly be exploring new altered states of awareness," I clarified.

"I don't care how you put it. It's wild. Maybe it's even wilder than if you were sleeping around with a bunch of people," Tamara mused. "I mean, you want to find someone that having sex with him is going to help you know your soul...is going to help you go into other dimensions, like when you take some hallucinogen or something."

"Yes. Sacred sex," I affirmed.

"So how were you raised that you're so open to all this? It certainly never would have occurred to me in the slightest," Camille asked.

"I was not raised with any religion or any religious edicts in regards to sex as being immoral, shameful, or wrong. I had many boyfriends since I was seventeen and consider it a natural part of the relationship," I explained. "As long as I can remember, I always knew about sex; no one ever had to teach me and I never asked. I must have learned it through cultural mediums and through TV osmosis. I did sense it was something that was private, but not bad or wrong at all. So, when I played doctor or experimented with my little boyfriends and girlfriends between four and six years old, there was never any repression or shame attached. It was innocent curiosity and exploration."

"My father spanked me when he found me masturbating when I was six. Maybe that's why I'm so fucked up," Camille shared nonchalantly.

"That's so ignorant! Yes. I hate to say it, but that can fuck you up," La Bellina concurred.

"One time I was a little tired and weirded out by a five-year-old girlfriend who always wanted me to be the king and she was the queen who had been 'bad'," I related. "Then she would want me to forcefully pull down her pants and punish her with spankings. So Japanese, it's classic. I was able to go and complain to my mother about the masochistic game my Japanese girlfriend liked to play, because we had a completely open dialogue on these matters. I think I was tired of being the king more than anything. I had to do all the work. Something made me feel uneasy about the role-playing and when I spoke to my mother about it she didn't flinch. She just told me that if I didn't feel good about it not to do it. My grandmother took it a step further in making a joke about it every time that girlfriend would come over she would say: "*Allí viene la china cochina*," which translates from Spanish; "Here comes the dirty Chinese girl." But it rhymed in Spanish, so it was funny and we'd all laugh."

"How cool. You were so lucky to have parents like that," Camille said.

"Even going back to four-years old, I remember I used to have a collection of playboy centerfolds in my "office", which I kept under my father's desk. My grandfather, who lived with us, had Playboy magazines and my brother and I knew there was something "special" about them so we'd go in and steal them. It wasn't even sexual to me. I just wanted what I saw adults treated as "special" and secretive. I also took empty pill bottles and collected my nail clippings, pretending they were pills. I got that from my Dad who always had a million medicines and vitamins. I was just emulating my elders."

"You didn't swallow your nails like they were real pills, did you?" Tamara asked disgusted.

"No, of course not! It was just play," I responded. "One day, my mother and my maternal grandmother played a joke on my other grandfather who was very modest, and was not the one who collected the Playboy magazines, by taping up a Playgirl centerfold on a closed door of his room to see his reaction. They hid behind another door spying to catch the moment my grandfather discovered the nude male poster. But I found it first! "Just what I always wanted!" I exclaimed. Delighted, I went to great pains to get a chair, climb up on it, and take it down. I then triumphantly marched off to add it to my collection. My mother and grandmother just had a good laugh and let me have it. Neither one ever said a word to me."

"Oh, how adorable. I can imagine you marching off with your nude centerfold so happy. And it wasn't even sexual to you. Kids are so funny," La Bellina said.

"When I was a teenager and all my friends were experimenting and starting to have sex it scared me, not making out, but intercourse. All of my friends had lost their virginity, except me, but I was fine with it. I wasn't comfortable with having sex yet, so I was fine being the odd man out. Then when I was seventeen, I woke up one day and I was ready! Just like that, the fear was gone! I was excited to take on a new aspect of myself and the prospect of exploration was a grand adventure and I took the bull by the horns, literally," I shared with my captive audience.

"Oh, no, I'm not sure I want to hear how you took the bull, literally," Tamara said laughing.

"I've never heard the story of your first time," La Bellina said.

"I had many boys who were interested and one day at a party at my house, it was my parents party, but both my brother and I had invited a few friends; I found one of the boys a few years older hot. He made a clear play for me and I went with it. I took him into my bedroom ready and willing for everything," I confided.

"Listen to you. You were on a mission," Tamara laughed.

"I was ready to play and have fun! I remember I had a renaissance dress on. I think I thought it was festive party attire even though no one else was in costume. We made out and riled each other up and got all juicy but just when it was the moment for actual getting naked I stopped. I went into the bathroom and changed into a cowboy outfit: a hat, gloves, cowboy boots, and a G-string. I came out topless and I got on top of him. I was waving my arms around saying things like 'Ride 'em, cowboy! Giddy up!' and 'I'm a bronco buster!'"

"No! Suraya! You really did take the bull by the horns!" La Bellina said as she and the girls bust up laughing.

"You went from being scared to that overnight?" Camille asked.

"Yep. When I'm ready for something, I'm leading the way," I said enthusiastically. "I'm glad I waited 'til I was really ready, because I had so much fun. Out of all my girlfriends I had the best time losing my virginity. I think they were too young and most of their stories sounded so awkward and boring. The guy I was with didn't think I was a virgin. He couldn't believe it. When you're comfortable, its natural."

"I bet he couldn't believe it! So, did you fall in love?" Camille asked.

"No. He wanted to date, but I only wanted to see him one more time and then I lost interest," I said. "He didn't captivate me enough for me not to want to explore."

"You sound like the guy, but I understand that. You either have that chemistry or you don't," La Bellina said.

"I went out into the dating world not with the idea of finding love or a boyfriend, but truly just excited about exploring and experimenting adventurously. As fate would have it, only after dating a handful of people, I fell in love just a few months later. It literally was a little voice in my gut that said: 'Ah, this is what I was really looking for.' I was surprised by the voice, because I was having fun and not expecting it at all. From then on, I was in one love relationship after another and no longer cared about just "experimenting," it had to have a connection. And my family let my first boyfriend come and live with us for six months when he was in between places. My brother's girlfriend lived with us too at some point."

"Wow! Now that is an accepting family!" Camille said, her face looking like it had been eroded of all her old preconceived notions by a wave of understanding of what is possible in the world of sex, love, and family.

"So, no, I was not raised with any kind of programming about sex being something that was bad or to be limited in any way, from which the inner voice demanding "sacred sex" could have morphed from either a rebellious reaction or a moralistic family programming. All these messages about being more selective with choosing an energetically compatible partner to cultivate this flowering of energy awareness is coming from a very deep, wise, intuitive place that has nothing to do with my upbringing. It is as if my cells, the energy itself is letting me know that it needs to thrive and explore my potential. I was caught off guard by this message of needing "sacred sex." A type of sexual play and intimacy that I realized I hadn't experienced completely in any of my relationships until my experience with Thad and the kundalini opening allowed me to achieve emotional abandon and pure bliss."

There was a moment of stunned silence prompted by all my lofty ambitions of spiritual sexuality that I think never occurred to them. Why should they, if they never occurred to me before?

"Well, I guess you're ready and you know what you want and you're just out there finding a bull you can grab by the horns. Suraya rides again!" Tamara quipped and the girls broke out giggling again."

"Well, it sounds beautiful to me. I want sacred sex. Teach me," La Bellina said with a sweet but sly smirk.

"Actually, it sounds like you can't grab any old bull to experiment anymore. Maybe it won't be so hard. You just have to teach them," Tamara suggested.

"Teaching someone physical things is fine," I said. "But how do you teach real emotional honesty, acceptance...trust? I can't go to that place of vulnerable ecstasy if I have to protect or defend myself from a lover emotionally. Even a subtle wall of psyche defense would drain the surplus of energy needed for venturing into the outer limits of exploring the new state of consciousness during sex or in my own path. The stakes are higher now for me not to waste my energy, because the rewards are so much greater too."

"It sounds wonderful, but I'm going to stick to good old-fashioned cowboy boots, bronco-busting sex. This is all too much for me," Tamara said.

"Oh, I still like that too. I'm just expanding my repertoire," I replied wondering how much of my experience they actually believed.

"Don't get me wrong. I'm ready for sacred sex bliss too. I just think it's gonna be too much work to teach a wild bronco all this," Tamara said laughing.

"Tell them the story of the cute Swami who wanted you to be his sex teacher and wanted you to live on his peanut farm," La Bellina implored trying to prolong story-telling time.

"His peanut farm? Was he wealthy?" Camille asked.

"Oh, come on. How much money could you make in peanuts?" Tamara mocked. "No pun intended."

"Jimmy Carter was a peanut farmer and I heard he had some dough," Camille scoffed. "Duh. Peanut butter is huge. Kids' favorite, if it doesn't kill them from an allergy."

"The Swami said he would support her and wanted her to live on his peanut farm," La Bellina said, trying to queue me.

"When I thought about it for a millisecond, because the Swami was cute, I thought what kind of authentic Indian life experience could I have in this situation. I pictured myself in the lush, beautiful farm setting that was the area I knew his farm was located in. It truly was set in a wondrous place that I loved best in all of my travels in India so far. I thought I'd learn about farming and dedicate myself to my spiritual practices. I wanted to ensure a real countryside Indian experience, but I didn't know just how to convey that desire. Flustered, all I could think of was to ask him if I could drive my own oxcart around the plantation. I had a romantic image of me riding my oxen to the watering hole after playing with the vegetables in the field," I said dazed by the memory of my own comedic innocence as La Bellina and the girls laughed out loud.

"A fucking oxcart? That was the deal breaker, your one condition?" Tamara asked. "You should've been asking for your own peanut farm!"

"Most girls ask for a Mercedes and you ask for an oxcart!" La Bellina chimed in. "I would send you a little Mercedes symbol to put on the oxen's head," La Bellina continued to laugh.

"I'd never driven an oxcart before and I wanted to live out an exotic Indian lifestyle. I thought it was romantic. Somehow the life on the farm would connect me to the earth," I said.

"She's a little different," La Bellina said through affectionate chuckles.

"Well, that whole Swami incidence is a story for another time, girls." "But I will tell you, I never went to live on his peanut farm and ride around in an oxcart."

20

"Sake and the Séance"

As my practitioner-training course progressed with Thad so did my relationship unfold with "The Widower." The "Silver Fox" had left to travel around the world, Wolfgang had gone to live in China and as far as the other gentlemen with whom I was set up, the chemistry was not pulling me. Nevertheless, the Widower kept furiously spinning a sticky web to keep drawing me in.

I could've kept looking, but The Widower and I had that pulling, sparkly chemistry, mutual spiritual interests and sense of humor; and he was sweeping me off my feet. So, against my misgivings of dating a widower and against my inner voice that had told me he was a sneaky, "sneaky bad," sleazy producer that didn't tell the truth about what he did, I decided to jump right in.

This type of intuitive voice was new to me. The way it would pop up out of "nowhere" so clearly without any "tangible" evidence made it hard to believe. After all, he had traveled halfway around the world to an Indian Ashram where I ran into him just to get blessings. That had to be a pure-hearted, spiritual man, right? Or maybe he had done so many dark things in his life that my inner voice was trying to warn me with "sneaky bad" that he felt he needed extraordinary help from the universe. I was going to find out.

The guests started arriving for a Friday dinner party followed by a séance. He apparently had been having weekly séances for many months now. I understood they started when he had contacted his deceased wife through one of these séances and then he was hooked.

The Widower was a man of his house and always directed the help in putting out the good china and fresh new flower arrangements throughout the house for his parties. The guest list was comprised of the usual "players" in these séance chronicles and a few varied guests that would add a new flavor to the evening each week.

The list of regulars started with a handsome, tall, Nordic, thirtyish man, Jarrid who was the Widower's best friend. Jarrid was also The Widower's right-hand man in a new production company in which they were going to produce T.V. shows on spiritual healers, psychics and channelers.

Then there was the channeler, Clare, who would preside over the evening entertainment and séance, and her galumph of a husband, Oscar. I understood he always had to be present to protect his wife physically since she would go into trance and let Spirits from beyond and other worlds speak through her. I was never sure if he was protecting her from us or from the Spirits who spoke through her. If some guy got emotional about her dealing out ill tidings and accosted Clare, the husband could restrain him, but how could he protect her from a belligerent Spirit that had possessed her body? He couldn't punch his wife in the eye to ward off the poorly behaved Spirit, right? Now that would've been funny!

Then there was a frail, world-renowned, British psychic, Albertine, and his gay lover, Mace. Albertine was going to be one of the featured psychics in the shows The Widower was going to produce.

This was to be my first session with them. The other two guests were Jarrid's, pretty, petite, though slightly square Asian girlfriend, "Sake," and our mutual friend "The Guru Agent."

Well, the evening was off to a rollicking start. Sake was demure at dinner and The Guru Agent seemed to have an instant crush on her. After a few drinks she started to flirt back very saucily with him, thirsty to be the center of attention. Jarrid didn't seem to care about his girlfriend's change in behavior, but instead laughed about it with The Widower, who kept raising his eyebrows at me as if it was an "in joke" as he tried to encourage the little Guru Agent's flirtatious attention.

Albertine, in his proper English well-mannered way had several stories of royalty or very famous celebrities for whom he had provided psychic readings. Clare, the medium, was smiley and nice, but there was nothing special about her and she didn't say much. Her style was outdated and frumpy. Big flower print, long skirt and vest over a buttoned-up 1800's prairie-style blouse. And her hair was a brittle blond that needed a good conditioning treatment. Her husband gave me the willies, though, like a corrupt member of the clergy. All the spiritual stuff was just a business. Not that he said anything to support that; it was one of those intuitive feelings, again.

Then Clara's husband started drooling over Sake, too, and it turned into a competition between him and The Guru Agent vying for her attention. It seemed to fuel the comedic flames even more for Jarrid and The Widower. I was laughing in disbelief at the whole scene. It was so odd how these grown men vied so blatantly, one in front of his wife, and both of them ignoring the fact that she had a boyfriend. I don't know what they saw in her really. I mean she looked like a block. I don't even think they liked her all that much. I think it was more like some juvenile game that had to be won for the sake of winning.

The Guru Agent was the most asexual, anti-relationship person I'd ever met. He had always shared with friends the details of his intimate life. He hadn't had sex or a girlfriend in ten years or more. He once confided in me that he didn't like going down on any woman and was too afraid of germs to have any intercourse casually, even with a condom, so sex couldn't have been driving him. Men and their facades and egos. I guess he was keeping up appearances, but what was the other shmuck's excuse? His wife's ugly skirt? Just like Jarrid, Clare didn't seem to care.

* * *

We all sat quietly around Clare in the living room as she made space for the Spirits to enter her body. I'd been to a few very famous channelers in the past and I was never that impressed. The information was either too general or didn't ring true and I never felt any special presence around any of them. Maybe I simply never met the real deal.

A guru whose life and teachings I respect greatly, Parma Hansa Yogananda, said that only lower astral beings use people's bodies to communicate. Yoganada said that a truly high dimension being has the ability to communicate with each individual directly if it chooses.

The Widower pointed out how nervous Jarrid was with enjoyment.

"Hello, everyone," the entity spoke.

"We are well and who may ask has come to speak with us tonight," replied The Widower.

"It's Racer X," replied the entity—a pseudonym to protect even the Spirit players.

"I thought I recognized your voice," The Widower continued. Believe me, there was no voice change. It was bland, old puddie-toots Clare talking in her lower register.

"I see Jarrid has had the courage to come back. I'm pleased," Racer X-Puddie-toots-Clare said with her eyes closed. Jarrid giggled nervously and slouched down and away from her in his chair as if he may be smacked at any moment.

"Yes. Well Of course I came back," Jarrid said.

"...Yes, but you almost didn't. You are afraid to keep looking at the truth. And you're worried I was going to get on you for not doing your homework."

"No. I did do what you said."

"And the dreams?"

"I'm still having the same nightmares. Endless battles, and I'm chopping heads and limbs."

"Yes. Well, you were a warrior in too many lives and you're afraid to look at who you were, because you're afraid of becoming that person again in this life. You're tired of the blood," Racer X affirmed.

"I did what you said, but the nightmares won't stop. What happened?" asked Jarrid. The Widower leaned in and whispered to me that Jarrid's dreams were causing him anxiety and an almost post-traumatic stress disorder was developing. He suffered from anxiety attacks and nervous twitches had developed. I hadn't noticed any twitches, yet. He looked like a persecuted child in his seat.

"You did not commit yourself fully. You did it half-ass. You still rebel, because you don't want to believe in who I am, and who you are. It's all too much for you still," Racer X chided.

"Who are you, again?" asked Jarrid.

"Never mind who I am! Who are you Jarrid?!!" Racer X raised his voice in a surge of passion. Jarrid shrank as he pushed his six-foot-three frame into the chair, trying to escape Racer X's admonitions.

"This is about you accepting the pain and suffering you have caused in your past life and knowing you will not resort to such violence in this life. I'm not a stupid child to let you pull one over me. I see all. You are the stupid child who is not willing to do as I tell you. You squirm in your seat afraid of me and yet you do not believe who I am. You are afraid of your own black-hearted past that you dream about nightly. And you are a lying rat."

I felt The Widower hold back his laughter and although I understood how he could find all this funny if he were an objective observer, I thought it was strange if he really took this whole séance seriously. I also was flummoxed how he relished in his friend being berated. Racer X continued to talk at Jarrid:

"I know you are suffering, so I have patience." Racer X finished berating this dreamtime villain and turned to address the group.

"I'm beyond your comprehension. I'm from the Neeweesh Galaxy, that is so distant, you do not know it exists. We are all much more advanced than you. We do not have bodies as you know them. Now, does anyone have a question?" Racer X continued.

In between answering questions in a predictably general way, Racer X would go back to berate Jarrid.

"Ah ha! You're thinking about what I've said in your little rat brain, but you must stop thinking so small. You must think in a larger, more expansive manner and then you will grow. Do not stay with a puny Oompah Lumpah brain. In that big head of yours it will rattle around and scramble. You will have a breakdown," Racer X said, belittling Jarrid and then returning to answer questions from the rest of the group in a totally respectful, non-condescending way.

It was so strange how Jarrid allowed this "entity" to treat him in such an insulting way and put him down in front of everybody. Racer X did give others advice or tell them that they might be on the wrong track about something in their lives, but never did anyone get the berating that Jarrid did. The entity said nothing to The Widower. And The Widower seemed to get a sense of voyeuristic satisfaction in that Jarrid and company could be so exposed by this Spirit. I found the whole thing to be so personally intrusive into people's lives, especially in a group setting.

"Good bye everyone. It was so nice to meet with you all," Racer X said and then bland Clare, Puddie-toots, shuddered a bit and opened her eyes.

"Hello. How was it? Who came through, tonight?" Clare asked as bland and fake as her muted, made-in-China with God knows what chemicals, flower print skirt. She acted as if she was waking up from a refreshing nap and had no clue what was said.

"Racer X came through," The Widower said nodding his head in approval.

"Oh, one of the big guns," Clare said.

"Yeah, and the guns were all pointed at me," Jarrid said with a disturbed chuckle.

"You're lucky that Racer X has taken such special interest in working with you," The Widower said emphatically as we all moved to the dessert buffet.

"How could you get such enjoyment out of that spirit insulting your friend like that especially if Jarrid is taking it so seriously?" I asked.

"My dear, he needs it to grow. It's for his own good. He doesn't listen and doesn't do what he's told by the spirits," he said very seriously and then let out a laugh just thinking about the whole episode.

Well, the battle for the Asian minx continued at the dessert table and as she reveled in the attention I noticed from across the room that she swayed a bit. She was getting louder and the strap on her dress kept falling off her shoulder, adding to her suitors' amusement. I think they all thought that her coquettish body language spoke to them individually. Apparently, it didn't occur to the men that her escalating coquettish body language escalated with each drink of tequila. It's like confusing a strippers' lap dance for love. Sake was getting drunk. She made her way over to me on the couch, not to my liking.

"I'm coming to sit and talk to you, The Widower's beautiful girlfriend. You are so beautiful you know that?" Sake said, as I cringed to have to deal with her drunkenness.

"Thanks. That's sweet of you to say," I replied.

"I much prefer talking to you than to those louts," she said. "Girl talk. You seem nice. There is something very nice about you."

"You looked like you were sucking up the attention and enjoying twisting them around your fancy," I said.

"My fancy pantsy?" We laughed.

Then she looked me directly, intensely trying to focus her eyes balls that were marinating in tequila on me. She looked like she wanted something from me. I recognized that look. It was the look of someone with deep pain--a life's cross to bear pain.

"So, what do you want to talk about?" I asked, actually wishing she'd go away. She gave me the willies.

"I just want to be here with you...just talk...nothing really...but it's gotta be real. Not the bullshit I get from those guys," Sake delivered with warmth and a twist of caustic, acerbic tones.

She wanted real so I would give her real.

"I see pain in you. It's fresh in your eyes, right under the surface. The pain of abuse," I said softly in a low tone so the others across the room couldn't hear.

"Oh, my God! I knew you were special. How did you know? No one ever sees it. I knew I wanted to talk with you," she said as if I was a genie that had just been released from a magic lamp to fulfill her wishes.

"It's easy to see. You wanted me to see it. You offered the impressions through your eyes...and it's not mystical. It's obvious. Maybe most people just don't want to tell you the truth," I said.

"Ooohh! You're good. Good point. But not you, you tell it like it is...like me. We're not fake. I hate fake people! Most people are fake."

"So, what happened to you?"

"You know, I've had a very hard life. You have no idea. There was a time in my life that was so horrible that it was like I was pinned under a plank of wood," Sake said dead serious.

"Were you abused by your family?" I asked.

"By many people in my family. I wanted to die at one point. And I had nowhere to turn. I feel I can talk to you. I get this strange feeling you can help me. Like you know something. Are you a therapist or something? You're so beautiful, you know that?" said Sake as she swayed in close and provocatively as if she was imparting a confidential secret.

"Thank You. No. I'm not a therapist. But I'm good to talk to..."

"I want to tell you my story someday, but not here with all these leeches, weirdos, fakos...in private," she said as if she was sitting vulnerably on the edge of a cliff feeling the wind blow up through her from an endless emotional chasm below her.

"What do you do, then, you sexy angel?" The Minx inquired.

"Well, I'm working on several projects. I recently finished a script called "Sexual Healing" for a major production company," I explained on autopilot, as talking about oneself over and over can get boring.

"That sounds juicy, perfect," the Minx interjected. I ignored her comment and kept on in a more serious tone feeling her sexual engines revving up toward me, which I did not want to encourage.

"...but currently at the forefront of my efforts is a screenplay called "Brujas del Barrio," which is Spanish for Witches of the Hood. It's about a boy who lives in the shadow of his older brother who died a hero and his parents--in blaming themselves for his death--aren't able to fully be present and they check out emotionally to their younger sons. The sons get involved in the gang world until a fated encounter with a witch in the poor barrio brings the Spirit of the dead brother in contact with his living brothers. It's a journey of healing through the mystical, magical guidance of the dead brother's ghost. The witch lures the boys into spiritual realms and away from the gangster life and ultimately allows the parents to forgive themselves and free the spirit of their older son and allow him to move into the afterlife in peace."

"Wow! A smart, sexy angel. What a power punch. I like it. Brew House del Bar...EO...wow great story," she said, studying her speech as she spoke obviously not sure she was getting it right in her drunkenness.

"Brujas del Barrio. Witches from the Hood. It has nothing to do with beer and brewing, no kegs involved." I kinda laughed as I explained. "But funny, that is the other title we were thinking of because of witches' brew..."

"...I like you. In fact, I love it. We should all go to Santa Barbara!"

"Yeah. That could be fun. Well, we should ask the guys when it's a good time for them to get away from work," I said.

"Fuck them. I don't have to ask them anything. I don't ask. You and I can just go alone. Fuck them. Let's just go and fuck it up! It'll be so fun. We can just fuck it up. OK?"

The Asian minx had the hots for me apparently. I glared at The Widower signaling him to intervene as Sake inched her way closer to me practically sitting on my lap. I could see him holding back his laughter, again, at the drama that had unfolded of the "bottled-spirits" kind this time. The

Widower certainly entertains himself with his sense of humor which actu-ally reminds me of myself, always laughing at the crazy, unpredictable dra-mas in life. Trying to squelch his laughter, he directed Jarrid to intervene.

Jarrid came and peeled her off of me.

"It's time to go, Sake," Jarrid spoke to her in that funny voice adults use to speak to toddlers when warning them of impending punishment.

"No. Me and her are going to fuck it up in Santa Barbra." Sake's bra strap fell in a grand finale gesture and her breast popped out to salute us all farewell. "Good night everybody. Thank you! I had a wonderful time!"

We all laughed. I think Racer X, the channeled spirit, should have given Sake some advice on her drinking, or perhaps on how to fix her shoul-der strap, or most importantly how to heal the abuse that was running her raw and unsettled her life, instead of berating her boyfriend for nothing all evening. It was an affair to remember in jest, an odd joke to share with friends and also an affair to forget in regards to giving its merit any cre-dence. The night will be remembered like a bad dream of foul spirits caused by cheap, rancid Chinese take-out.

21

"Family Flair"

Goggles, gloves, sander whirring, ready, set, go! I had decided some room doors and cabinet doors needed sanding and refinishing and painting and as usual, I thought it couldn't be that difficult.

I was outside in the yard, my sand plainer pressed down on the door whirring away as the layers of old varnish and damaged layers shredded off. I stopped to accesses the work and it was even and looking smooth, a peach-fuzz feel to the cleaned wood was resulting. Finally, a handy job I think I can handle! Again, through my being I felt a surge of that strong, vigorous sense of can-do spirit that makes me feel I can rise up to meet the world at the survival level. Maybe I should start taking this feeling as a warning sign that I should stop doing the new venture at hand before I ruin yet another piece of the house!

I decided to sand down more layers to be thorough, as some of the whitewash was imbedded deeper into the grain in places. I kept sanding and soon realized I was making the door half as thin as it was originally and perhaps I should stop. It was one of those mostly hollow doors and I was wearing it down quick. Oh, no! Here it goes, again--an apparently simple job possibly turning the corner into a mild, yet exhausting catastrophe!

I read the whitewash instructions and applied it with direction per fection on a corner of the door. It looked horrible, blotchy and way too white, but I figured it needed to sit a few hours to see the final result.

"Hi Micha!" My Pa said coming out to great me in the yard. "Oh, it looks like she's busy on another one of her jobs," he said, patting my back and smiling. My mother emerged from the house.

"So just to remind everyone that your uncle Hogart and aunt Ellen are coming to stay with us a couple of days. Oh, your uncle will love that you're doing handy work. Even though they have money, he does everything around his house. He'll jump in and help you out," my mother twittered.

"Ok, Great! Good to know. I already forgot," I said, half-preoccupied with how bad my whitewash job of the door looked. "Well, I'd like to get this little project done before they come so that things look nice."

"Yeah, he's crazy, but everyone loves uncle Hogart," my mom said. "He's nuts, but you really feel he cares."

"Ok, let's go. I can't look at this door anymore; it's driving me nuts!" I said and herded everyone to go their own way and to get to what they needed to do. "Move on little doggies," I teased.

I drove down to the gym while the whitewash set.

"Hey Sursurayray!" Mancho yelled out from the Café and waved me over to visit with him as I entered the gym.

"Hey Mancho," I said and went over to say hello for a second.

"So, when are we going out?" he asked, not missing a beat from our last visit weeks ago. He pulled out a stool and sat me down next to him.

"Hey, did you get the idea to lure me into a sexual situation by helping you with a supposed ED…" I said as he interrupted.

"…I do have ED. The most beautiful woman could be standing naked in front of me and I wouldn't get an erection," he reiterated excitedly out loud for all to hear as I rolled my eyes.

"I know. I guarantee you have no problem with the function of your junction," I said, and he laughed.

"Good one, function of your junction," he said. "But it's true. I take Viagra."

"Did you get that idea from that movie "Some Like It Hot" where Tony Curtis invents a story that he is sexually numb after the death of a fake fiancée, in order to get a sympathetic Marilyn Monroe to help him with his problem, which naturally involved her kissing him to see if she can inspire his junction?" I said knowingly and Mancho couldn't help but laugh.

"Yeah, kinda" he spit out, quickly caught, but reveling in his mischievous ways.

"Yeah, I figured," I said laughing too. Who couldn't laugh at "clown boy's" overly theatrical attempts at seduction.

"So, go out with me. We'll have fun, I promise," he said, a little more straightforward.

"Like I said, I don't date guys with ED. Got to get to working out," I said as I got up to leave. "See ya!"

"I'm going to get you! You'll see. One of these days!" he yelled out without shame or shyness of anyone overhearing any part of our conversation.

I hurried back home after a quick workout to check my whitewash door and it looked exactly as it had before. I sanded off the whitewash area again and white washed it again three different ways, diluting the wash each time and it still looked like crap! Hell, I can't keep sanding the door it's getting too thin! Is it time for me to realize as I botched yet another household repair job. Perhaps I should throw in the towel with these dreams of self-sufficiency?

Hell no! I put the room door aside and went on to take all four closet doors off to sand and repaint, two things I've proven to be a bumbling failure at. I sanded into exhaustion and painted them white. I let them dry overnight.

The next morning, I went out to view the final result. They all looked perfect! Lo and behold I finally did something that looked good! I had a moment of Martha Stewart perfection and homemaker elation. I felt like a salt of the earth, hearty, pioneer woman for once in my loins. I could survive on the prairie! As I basked in my first accomplishment, I took out the room door once again and stared it down like an experienced hunter to see how I would tackle it.

Then it came to me! The wise thing to do was to buy another room door and have it whitewashed by a professional. Ha! And so that's what I did. To my surprise and relief, it took the professional a few tests to get it right. Staining is more of an art than I thought.

Before I hung the hallway cabinet doors back in place it dawned on me that I should be thorough and sand and repaint the frame of the cabinet. Why not make everything match perfectly, right?

So I sanded away and very quickly I learned that sanding a vertical object with an electric sander is not so easy as when it is horizontal. The end result of the frame turned out to be something I did not intend: smooth, but undulating, as if I was trying to evoke the idea of waves on wood, a creative ocean theme for a beach house perhaps, but I was not aiming for that in this case.

Oh, well, I'd had enough after trying to correct the undulations with a couple of sanding passes. I gave up being a perfectionist in doing the frame and decided that no one would ever notice the waves anyway. The cabinet frames in the hallway are wavy to this day.

I hung the doors up and another house repair job was behind me just in time for my aunt and uncle's visit. Something to be proud of!

"Look Jamie, look Hogart," said my mom pointing towards the hallway cabinet. "Suraya did it all by herself with no help or instruction." God knows I should've had some instruction. Ha! "She's the handyman in the family. Like her grandpa Waldo."

"Great job!" my Pa said and he put his hand on my shoulder proudly, as Waldo was his father.

"Hey, That's a pretty good job!" Hogart said inspecting the cabinets a little closer. "At least someone in this family has some gumption to learn how to take care of things so they don't fall apart. Uncle Hogart will help you while he is here if there is anything else you want to do, since no one else will," he chuckled, as he looked at my father. "Only Jimbo here would have the house falling around his head and he still wouldn't lift a finger."

"Yeah, I have other more important things to do," My Pa replied. "I'm glad to leave that work to you," he said with a grin, unapologetically and with some arrogance as if that kind of work was beneath him.

"Yeah, you're too lazy," Uncle Hogart said taunting him.

"Yes, your uncle will help. He loves to do all these things around the house," Aunt Ellen said.

"Wait a minute," Uncle Hogart said studying the hinges of the cabinet just as we were all headed to the dining room for dinner.

"What? What is it Gordis?" Aunt Ellen said. *Gordis* in Spanish is a loving name for "fat one" like saying Chubbsies.

"You put the hinges on backwards!" Uncle Hogart exclaimed. "I can't believe it! How did you do this?" he said and we all laughed.

"What?" I said studying the hinges. I couldn't figure out why they were backwards. They looked normal to me and they worked! "I'm not sure what I did wrong, but they work fine, can't I just leave them that way?" I said in utter disbelief and befuddlement that I couldn't figure it out.

"No. No. It should be done," he said to my comforting relief. We headed on to dinner.

"I think I'm going to retire from handy work," I said.

"No don't do that you'll be as worthless as your father in household matters then," Uncle Hogart said teasing. "Just be patient with yourself. You've got the right spirit and that's the most important thing."

"Yeah, she always jumps headfirst when she decides to do something," my mom said.

"Yeah, and sometimes she blows things up while she's at it," My Pa said teasing and we all laughed.

We all sat down to eat. Now, how should I describe good ole Uncle Hogart? He is a little bit of a caustic Archie Bunker but it's mainly in jest as he is sweet and not sour. He's an East Coast conservative with a lot of heart. He loves to hassle liberals. And my family tends to be liberal, so the banter is endless.

"So what are you liberals up to nowadays? Ruining the country? You know Suraya if you were smart, you'd listen more to your Uncle Hogart and not your sappy, intellectual, commie parents. The liberals have ruined the country. Wake up and smell the coffee."

"Oh, Gordis please, we're going to eat now," Aunt Ellen said laughing. "You can beat them all up after dinner."

"Ok, let's eat! Who's going to do the prayer? Jim?" he said with a snicker knowing fully well my Pa doesn't pray.

"Don't ask him to do the prayer. He will do a prayer you'll never forget," I said laughing.

"What's the old man going to do, moon me?" Uncle Hogart said.

"Gordis behave, no fighting with Jim," Aunt Ellen said with a warning and a laugh.

"It's alright. We're just all having fun here," Uncle Hogart said. "Ok, Jim, now I really want to see you lead the prayer when your daughter says that I will never forget it."

"Pa's going to do his prayer?" my brother said as he flew into the room as if the wind was on his back, guitar case in hand in his usual Indiana Jones jungle-looking attire. "Hello everyone! Looks like I'm just in time for the festivities."

"Oh, look, Nico has arrived!" my mother said as if she was a professional crier announcing distinguished guests at a ball. "Hi love!"

"Hi Mom," Nico said as he put down his guitar case behind his chair and went around greeting everyone at the table with a kiss.

"Where are you headed to, Machu Picchu, man?" Uncle Hogart joshed.

"Ha! Yeah, I learned to dress like this from my trips to the jungle and I liked it. Most practical: light, lots of pockets and easy to wash," Nico answered proudly.

"Just kidding. You look great kid!" Uncle Hogart assured.

What can I say about my brother? He's the fastest reader, besides my father, that I've ever seen. He will read to you every time he has a chance, even while you're hiking. He has brown curly hair and is often confused for Ben Stiller. He tortured me teasing me as a child but we are good friends through it all since we shared so many great memories as partners in crime in our exotic family travel adventures. We have the same sense of humor and love for travel, different cultures and learning. One thing that amazes me about him and what sets us apart is that he can be surrounded by extremely negative people and he isn't affected. He can ignore the negativity and always maintain being positive and happy, regardless. I, on the other hand, am greatly drained by negative people in my life. I don't know which of us is the wiser.

"Hey Nico, good to see you. How you doing man?" Uncle Hogart said with a jivy cadence.

"Good. Can't you tell?" Nico said chuckling as he opened his arms out to his sides showcasing himself and then stoked his fine jungle clothes showcasing all his fineness in jest. "You guys look good too! So, what's this about Pa's prayer?" he said, ready to jump into the spirit of good mirth.

"Come on, Nico, you know Pa's blessing. His special dinner blessing," I insisted, as I sent him memories telepathically of our good man's gracious ways.

"Oh, oh, yeees! The blessing. Oh, good. I'm just in time." Nico said setting himself down in a chair. "Yes, give us the blessing Pa. Proceed!" He waved his arm in a grand gesture to continue.

"Ok, here goes," my Pa said. He moved his hand like he was crossing himself but with a flare and flurry and jazz-hand finger twinkling that looked more like the moves of a stoned magician. "Bibbidy Babidi Boo! Ex Pax Nabisco!" he said, as if it was a Latin benediction. And with a straight face at the end of those nonsensical goofy words he strung together he gave the finger to everyone, he flipped us a bitch, gave us the bird and then laughed maniacally. Uncle Hogart and I busted up too.

"Oh Jim!" my mother said, as she kept her poise and manners while she laughed lightly.

"Oh my! That's sacrilegious! Did you just give us the finger, Jim?" Aunt Ellen exclaimed with laughter.

"Oh, Jim! You always take it too far," my mother said trying to hold a sense of propriety but allowing herself to go along with the laughter as long as everyone else took it with good humor.

"I guess you never were that pious choirboy, were you Jim? Aren't you afraid you're going to go to Hell for such things? Showing such disrespect for the man upstairs?" Uncle Hogart said.

"I don't believe in the man upstairs. Only weak saps do," my Pa stated firmly.

"Ohhh! Weak saps? So I'm a weak sap, Jim? Thanks!" Uncle Hogart said laughing. Even though they disagreed, they got a kick out of each other always.

"When I was a kid about six," my Pa explained, "my parents dressed us up, gave us some money for the donation basket and sent us to Sunday school, which was just a few blocks away through an alley. Well, we weren't going to go listen to that crap. We went and bought candy at the store and played in the alley. We got playing with sticks of course and I thought it was a good idea to flick some shit on my little brother," my dad said laughing, all wrapped up in the memory. "Then my brother flicked tar on me and it broke out into a full-blown tar and dog crap battle before you knew it. You know how boys are."

"So what did they say when you arrived all dirty at Sunday school? Did they kick you out? You would've deserved it, you little cretin," Uncle Hogart said.

"You must've driven your mother nuts, Jim," Aunt Ellen said laughing.

"He and his brother were incorrigible as children," my mother added with her sweet but proper air.

"We never made it to Sunday school. We went back home covered with shit and tar all over our good suits," Pa said gleefully relishing in the memory. "I told my mom that we were back from Sunday school! They asked us how we liked it and we said it was fine. Well, then they said that was impossible because Sunday school hadn't even started yet. They knew what had happened when we came back soiled with crap and tar," my Pa said breaking down in laughter as we all laughed along with him at the troublemaking story of his youth.

"So, did they beat you? You needed a good whooping in my opinion," Uncle Hogart said laughing.

"Yeah, because you're mean and punishing like all those controlling priests and religious nuts," my Pa snapped back playfully. "No, they didn't beat us. They said that was the end of Sunday school because we obviously didn't want to go. They knew they couldn't force us."

"So you don't really believe in anything? Nothing?" Uncle Hogart persisted with real curiosity.

"How can you not believe in God, Jim?" Aunt Ellen chimed in.

"Not the God that religion teaches. Do I know ultimately that there isn't a God? No. Who knows, maybe there is some higher being and we have a soul that goes on. I don't know. But it certainly has nothing to do with that fear-mongering crap they teach in churches. Religions are responsible for so many horrific things throughout history, like suppressing knowledge, oppressing women, or causing wars. A bunch of bastards, that's what they are," my Pa spoke plainly, seriously, vehemently, for once in this comic escapade.

"So how did she come about?" Uncle Hogart asked my father motioning to me. "How do you feel about what your rude, nasty father says about God when you believe in God?"

"Yes, she's the spiritual one of the family," my mom said.

"I'm used to his beliefs. It doesn't bother me," I said. "It never swayed my opinion. He was always very supportive of whatever interests I wanted to pursue, even my spirituality. He even took me to see the Dalai Lama once when I was a kid. He fell asleep during his talk, which is what he does when he is bored, but he took me. If I wanted to see a shaman when we traveled he would take me. But one thing I will say is that there is a difference between religion and spirituality and my dad still has not gotten to the point of differentiating the two. I'm not religious, but I have a spiritual practice and I do believe in a higher Conscious Life Force Energy that is overseeing creation. I don't just believe it, I'm coming to know it," I said.

"Woohoo!" Uncle Hogart said. "That's heavy. Get a load of that Jim! That must be a real kick in the teeth to your old father," he said chuckling.

"No. I support her in whatever she wants to do. She's too smart. She'll come around eventually," Pa said keeping a mock straight face and then when we all busted up laughing, he joined in to enjoy his joke too.

"And how, pray, tell, are you coming to know it?" Uncle Hogart asked square on.

"Oh, I'm doing a new spiritual practice that is opening me up to such profound experiences" I said, and just as I spoke the kundalini energy started to rise up my spine, making me hot. I felt breezes of ecstasy gently blowing around my heart and I began to subtly relive the bliss. "It's actually blowing my mind at this precise moment," I said so sincerely, it seemed to catch Uncle Hogart's attention and he sobered up from his sarcastic line of quips for a moment and just stared at me waiting to hear more.

"Really? So what is this that you're doing, sweetie?" Uncle Hogart said.

"I can't talk anymore right now as it's just too personal and I want to keep it close to the vest right now. But I will share it one day," I said. I had no desire to put the new delicate sacred experiences I was having under Uncle Hogart's critical microscope. I didn't want to waste my energy debating or convincing anyone at this point. I knew there would come a time, the right time to put it all out there to share.

"Ok. Ok. I get it. It's private for now. How about you, Nico?" Uncle Hogart asked my brother.

"My religion, or God, is tolerance," he said without hesitation as if it was the most masterful answer and it should impress us all.

"Oh, ho, ho. Listen to Buddha over there," Uncle Hogart mocked and laughed. "Good answer, Nico. I like that." He nodded approvingly.

"I'm agnostic," my mother offered up. "But I tend to believe that when we die, it's the end," she said, even though she prays every time something is not going well and does aura healings on my brother and I when we don't feel well. I think somewhere along the lines of her life which included intersecting with my father, she came to the conclusion that as an intellectual, it wasn't cool to believe in God. She outwardly has made scientific theories her religion. But I know she has true faith underneath it all.

"And now for a little after-dinner entertainment in honor of Uncle Hogart and Aunt Ellen," my brother announced with a sense of fun and whimsy, as he pulled out his guitar from behind his chair: "Ok, everybody, sing along with me. This is for Uncle Hogart." He strummed a few times to get everyone's attention. "For he's a jolly good fellow…"

"Oh my God! He always plays this!" I exclaimed as I and everyone at the table joined in song.

"For he's a jolly good fellow, for he's a jolly good fellow, that nobody can deny." Everyone sang through fits of laughter. I started to pound the table to the beat and my father joined in the table tapping.

"Is it somebody's birthday?" Uncle Hogart yelled out above the song. "Who are we singing for?"

"For you!!" my brother and I answered simultaneously.

"Oh! But it's not my birthday!" Uncle Hogart said laughing as we all continued to sing.

"It's not for your birthday. It's to welcome you," my brother exclaimed.

"Oh!" Uncle Hogart exclaimed flattered and taken aback, once he understood. "Ahh! You guys are crazy! Thank you. I appreciate it. I accept. That's really sweet," he said laughing harder, then joined in. "For I'm a jolly good fellow, for I'm a jolly good fellow…"

My brother went right into a rendition of "La Bamba" which is always a hit at family gatherings. Strumming hard and flamboyantly, he almost seemed to jump out of his seat now and again as he sang out at the top of his lungs. The good old family spirit rose to the occasion and we all continued to sing.

"Micha, dance for us!" my mother yelled out.

"Dance with me," I said as I grabbed my mother's hand and pulled her up out of her chair. We tripped our first few steps until we established that I would be leading the dance.

"Common, Uncle Hogart!" I said as my mom motioned for them to join us.

"Eeeh! Ok. You guys are nuts!" Uncle Hogart said.

"Common Gordis, shake your tail feather," said Aunt Ellen, encouraging him to get up and join in as she got up.

"I'm too old. My tail feathers have been plucked or just plain fell off by now." Uncle Hogart kvetched.

"Oh, that's not true. We dance all the time," Aunt Ellen corrected him.

"I may dance, but it doesn't mean I have any tail feathers left," Uncle Hogart joked.

We pulled my father up to dance and all cut the rug to several songs that my brother performed like he was a rock-and-roll star. In this family people seem to get more expressive, carefree and raise the roof to a greater extent the older they get. I guess we all have the same appreciation for time. Time is precious and fleeting and you best let go and feel the joy as much as you can, whatever we individually believe. Stomping, singing, dancing, laughing, and having a good time is necessary soul food as we edge towards our end in life, each day having less time on this planet. My family will go down in flames of our own fancy and delight. It's one way to rage against the dying light of the body and go on dancing into God's light.

Uncle Hogart rehung the cabinet doors properly the following day so that the hinges weren't backwards. And I finally came to terms with the fact that my time was best spent doing other things than household repair projects that always turned out to be somewhat of a debacle. It was time to retire my self-sufficient, survival prairie fantasy. I may love nature and be a bit of a tomboy, but I learned I'm more the belle of the ball with white gloves type when it comes to brute chores. Someone else should do the sweeping, or with my luck, I'll inadvertently trip someone and break the broom at the same time.

22

"That Date"

"**H**i beautiful! I'm so glad you're here." The Widower said as he whisked me through the front door. "I missed you." He kissed me deeply and I knew it was time to fully explore the physical heat between us.

"First, I'm going to take you to one of my favorite restaurants, Urasawa!" he said and laughed a little maniacally as if he was going to get great pleasure out of corrupting me with this decadent meal.

We drove to the Rodeo Collection, a little mock European road on Rodeo drive in Beverly Hills. We took the elevator up to the third floor and it opened onto a minute Japanese restaurant. There were only two other couples and you could hear a pin drop. It was like entering a reverent place of worship.

We were greeted in whispers and shown to the sushi bar.

"They say this is the pinnacle of *omakase* dining in LA." The Widower leaned in and whispered to me: "Omakase in Japanese means to trust. The chef decides what to create for us."

They started with some simple pieces of sushi, but the fish was like no other I'd ever had. That's when you realize there is an art to selecting fish…and the chefs were masters here.

An amazing procession of dishes ensued. Oh, for the love of the abalone steamed in sake, the scallops and duck *foie gras shabu shabu*, but the real gem that brought me to my knees and introduced me to a new bar of culinary delight was the kobe beef, grilled over wood charcoal. Such succulent, juicy, marbled meat I never could've imagined!

You may say and think you've tried kobe, but American kobe is nowhere close to the high-end, freshly flown from Japan kobe. I know we picture angels that don't eat food and live off of air and light, but I've now changed my mind. I know angels must eat kobe as they would be naturally drawn to those bits of human creation that reminds them of heaven on earth.

"Everything is so amazing, but I could eat several orders of this," I said to The Widower as I savored the kobe to the point of meditation. "Now I know why it's so quiet in here: everyone is stunned by flavors, so overwhelmed by pleasure, they don't even want to speak; they can't speak. I feel stoned out of my mind from this great chef's food," I said and giggled. The Widower laughed and nodded his head in agreement and pleased to hear my response, as it was apparent he wanted to find ways to spoil me. We continued to eat in silence, totally satisfied.

We drove home without speaking much, still in the spell of the meal. What a great way to start a seduction! There is a time in a courtship were everyone knows it's that date that takes things to a new intimacy and exploration of sex.

Back at the house, The Widower took me upstairs where he had his massage table laid out. The seduction plan was apparently set in advance. And why not, since I had come to him seeking a tantric lover to begin with. This is where it was meant to start all along.

But by the way, conducting my search really was no different than looking for a boyfriend. I guess old habits are hard to break and I'm used to being courted for a relationship, not just a sexual affair. As long as he and I were clear that the tantric sex exploration was of primary importance at this stage, I was open to it all. So we began with the good ole massage seduction, but truly the food at Urazawa was the exquisite sensual seductive move of the evening that opened my senses to new and otherworldly possibilities. If the meal had been a hint of what was to come, I would be in tantric heaven.

He helped me take off my clothes and although he seemed like he was salivating with anticipation he also acted like a professional masseur. He wanted to build the tension. He rolled up his sleeves and began. He performed such professional strokes on me that I assumed he must have taken a massage course. The touch of a new lover was titillating, but having had hundreds of sports' massages, I felt his light touch wasn't affecting my muscles.

"Can you go deeper?" I said gently, trying to maintain the mood in the candlelit setting. To my surprise he laughed. He found my request amusing.

"Yes, ma'am!" he said and went deeper. He had a good touch, but it was too superficial.

"Can you go deeper?" I asked wondering if I should just go with his brand of wet-noodle arm approach instead. He laughed again in surprise at my request. He seemed almost in disbelief.

"I don't know if I can, but I'll try," he said. He acted like he was really getting down to business and exerting effort. It became obvious that he wasn't used to putting muscle into a massage and he started to giggle, as it was obvious he felt hapless to summon the strength I requested.

"You can take a lot. I've never met anyone that can take this," he said and giggled again. "I can't do it any harder." He eked out the words as his hands slipped off my body and he almost slipped right on the floor. We both busted up laughing. He especially got a good chuckle, a good sign of a healthy sense of humor.

I realized I needed to switch gears from the deep tissue massage I'm used to and let him do his superficial sensual massage. I was inadvertently getting in the way of the sensual mood.

"That was really good. Now you can do it softer," I said as if it didn't have to do with his lack of strength but my changing desires.

"Good! That's a relief. I don't want to end up on the floor again," he said and laughed at the scenario.

He went back to his gentle strokes and of course stopped at my butt to knead incessantly. The body heat between us rose and the sensual massage seduction was doing what it was supposed to.

Having surrendered to his specific form of massage, it was apparent that he was a master of the softer touch approach and it turned out to be an amazing massage. He asked me to flip over and with the tension from all the touching, he couldn't resist leaning down for deep kisses while he continued to work his hands that progressed into our budding tantric explorations. He was a good kisser and had sensual leanings, but something was missing. The flow! The flow of movement like a dance that would mold us into one another in shapes that you can't describe, where you can't decipher whose leg or arm is wrapped around what. It was the beginning and he was a generous lover, caring about pleasing me, so maybe there was another comfort level waiting to happen that would open the door into "the flow." For now, it was good for cliché sex and the chemistry kept me slinking down the path, returning for more.

The kundalini started to unwind my body in the sex act. The pleasure in my whole body was heightened since my opening and I felt more alive.

Then about a month into our exploration, when I reached orgasm, something new and awesome happened! A column of energy traveled up the center of my body from my orgasmic vaginal contractions and burst my heart open with love. Not love for The Widower, just a tremendous storage room of love that I was learning was inside me. That storage room of love is what is sacred in us all. I was merging with the sacred, again, and again, and again. This is where I wanted to go and beyond with my new sex exploration. I burst into tears. Then I went into a quiet meditative space and floated in my largesse of Spirit. We lay on each other like cozy puppies. The real initiation into sex having a new dimension, a tantric, spiritual-sexual union had finally begun with The Widower.

"I want you to move some of your things here so that you feel like this is your home," he said. "I already have a key for you so you can come and go when you like."

I felt the capacity for us to greatly fall in love. I was already falling for him too, so I was open to wherever the relationship may go. But I was concerned about what I had found in the woman's bathroom/dressing room in his master suite. He appeared to want to move forward with me when he really wasn't over his past.

"I would love to, but there is no space. All your deceased ex-wife's things take up all the room in the closet," I said. He gave me a robe and led me into the dressing room.

There it all was: purses, dresses, baby doll lingerie, stuff, and more stuff, that like a busy, gaudy wallpaper swallowed every bit of feeling of space.

"Man, you had bad taste in clothes," I said under my breath to The Widower's dead wife. Maybe she was around, for even I was addressing her, now.

The Widower smashed a bunch of blouses on a rack together leaving a couple of feet of hanger space and said: "See? We just have to move her stuff a bit."

"That's no space at all. Why don't you get rid of your ex-wife's things?" I asked as I stepped into a psychological mine field.

"Stop saying that! She's not my ex-wife," he snapped.

"Do you consider yourself married?" I asked starting to feel a tingling, as a part of me was detaching from my body. I didn't want to be there, but I am an Aries, I go in headfirst. I had to know.

He hesitated. He seemed to be tripping over his mental responses as he was obviously "caught."

"No. I just never got a divorce. She's just passed on."

I took him into the adjoining vanity room.

"There is no room in the vanity either. It's filled with her make-up," I said as I opened the bottom drawer and pulled out a brush filled with her blond hair. It was so morbid to me.

"You have brushes with her hair in it. How is that supposed to make me feel? Look, if you're not over her death, I understand. You have all the right in the world to grieve as long as you need to. But this is not a healthy environment for me to be in, surrounded by all your deceased wife's things, or to be in a relationship where you are not fully present. You take the time you need and when you feel you're done grieving, four months, six months, give me a call and if I haven't met anyone else, we can start fresh," I said with all the sincerity in the world.

"No. You're wrong. I'm completely over her. I don't even think of her. I've just been lazy and procrastinated," he said without a doubt.

"I'm not sure I believe you. If you can't get rid of her things, that means you're not over her," I insisted.

"I got lazy...and then I decided I'd wait until January when I'm getting the whole house painted and then I would do a big cleaning and throw it all out," he said logically, "but if it bothers you that much I'll have it thrown out immediately. I'll find the time in the next couple of weeks."

Sometimes when you're falling in love and you're starting to bond sexually you turn into a mule with blinders to avoid seeing that the building is on fire. I was becoming a mule with blinders.

"How long ago did she die?" I asked.

"She's not dead. She just passed on four months ago."

My throat instantly parched and I couldn't swallow. I coughed out my shocked response.

"Four months ago? That means we started dating two and a half months after she died?! I was told it was like a year ago. How can you be dating so soon? You definitely need more time to heal."

"I started dating a month after. Life goes on. It wasn't a good relationship to begin with. We struggled with her drug addiction and fought all the time. She said that if I left her, she'd kill herself. I finally couldn't handle it and threatened her with divorce. Two weeks later I rolled over in our bed one morning to find her blue and dead. It was so hard when she died. On top of it, the police were investigating me for her murder. They tried to get me to confess that I murdered her. I needed to move on from that pain as soon as possible and try to find some comfort."

"You can't possibly be ready for a relationship."

"I didn't think I'd fall in love so soon, either. But that's the case. I'm a hundred percent here for you and the past is the past. I'm over her." He kissed me lovingly and we went back to sleep.

The tantric experiment had ended up in a relationship pretty quickly.

The next morning The Widower made French toast. He liked to cook and serve me.

"I'm so glad you're partaking in our séances. I want to have a session with Thad to see what it is that you rave so much about," he said.

"Yeah? I have to warn you not to expect too much. Thad says that most people don't open up so quickly, that my instant and dramatic response is more of an exception, not the rule. I'll give you his number. I'm excited to see what happens."

"I'm not desperate for experience," he said. "I went to therapy for twenty-five years. I've gone the distance. My therapist finally said I was completely healed and we ended our professional relationship. He's one of my best friends now."

"What did you have to heal yourself from?" I asked.

"My mother. I had the worst mother. She was mentally ill. I hated her," he went on to tell a story of a most unaffectionate, narcissistic battle axe that cared about no one but herself. Besides being a terrible cook, she apparently didn't have one nurturing quality about her. I don't know why, but when people explain about how terrible their mother was, they find it hard to put it into words. Just like Lazy Boy, the disgruntled comedian, he didn't say much, but mimicked his mother by putting on these contorted, sour, demented faces.

"My therapist is a genius of a man. He is the number one, top therapist in Los Angeles," he pronounced.

"The top therapist, huh? How do they qualify that?" I asked.

"He just is…the best. Everyone knows it. If you asked around town that is what you'd hear."

"Well, I'd like to meet the top therapist who is a genius at his game. I love interesting people. Can you arrange a time for me to meet him?"

The Widower's face glazed over and his eyes narrowed. He looked suddenly transformed. Evil. And he spewed a venomous attack on me.

"No, I will not! How dare you ask to meet with my therapist? What do you really want to do? That's crossing a boundary!" he said to me with hate pulsing from his face. I was scared for a confused instant and then I realized he was lost in his mind of triggers and traumas. I could feel that he was not seeing me. It was like he was a bull who saw the red cape and he was going to charge. He was looking at someone else that had hurt him in his past, his mother, his ex-wife; I didn't know, but I did know he was looking through me, not at me.

This was a breakthrough for me. In the past I would have jumped on him like a Tasmanian devil and ripped him a new one for attacking me so irrationally. I would've broken up with him right there and then and not looked back. But now I could see the layers of the person. It was like I could see through him. Instead of being drawn into an argument, or feeling hurt or insulted as I would have in the past, I became calm, understanding. I could not take it personally, because it had nothing to do with me. A deep compassion came over me for him. I realized I had to help him see me again, bring him to the present by standing by him and giving him the space and chance to see.

"First of all, you said that he's not your therapist any more, that he's your friend. I only want to meet him because you made him sound so interesting. I am always interested in meeting people who are at the top of their field; and besides, I'm studying psychology and now have a special interest in the subject."

"What is it you really want to do?" He continued looking like a fire-breathing troll. Normally he looked like an older version of James Franco, but with bad posture.

"Someone hurt you, but it was not me. Look at me. I don't have an ulterior motive. It's me!" I looked at him unswervingly as he continued to seethe. Then just as quickly as his tantrum came, it seemed to clear. His breath started to regulate and his narrowed eyes widened, again.

"Why are you so defensive about me meeting your friend? You really over-reacted. Why?" I asked calmly. His delusional plane had landed and he was able to communicate honestly about what was going on in his head to provoke such strong reaction.

"My wife…when she was so high on drugs she'd get paranoid and jealous. She thought I was having affairs. She called Mitch, my therapist, and told him lies about me and tried to get private stories out of him about me. It was so inappropriate. I felt so violated. She had no boundaries!" As he shared this story it was as if he was telling it to himself and he realized that he was reliving something from his past and was mixing me up emotionally with his troubled, drug-addict wife. He looked a bit sheepish and embarrassed that he had let reality slip into his troubled past that had nothing to do with me.

Thank God the softness returned to his face. In the past, this kind of emotional reaction would have sent me running out of the relationship. But I had experienced such change and growth, my boundaries and patience seemed to have grown, too. I seemed to have more space inside of me to see more clearly and not take other people's triggers personally. From my recent transformations I had a new belief in how the human Spirit can grow and evolve so I had all the faith that he would be healed of this tragic last relationship. So much for the twenty-five years of therapy, you're 100% healed, huh?

The Widower danced over to a corner of the kitchen counter, picked up a key and handed it to me.

"This is the house key. I want this to be your home too," The Widower said and kissed me.

Was this a key to his heart or a key to Pandora's Box with the grief of his dead wife imprinted in her belongings, festering in that house?

23

"Back at Butterfly Valley Another Cocoon Cracks"

It is said that we only use 5% of our brain and have a great capacity of mental ability as of yet untapped. As the experience continued to unfold, I have come to believe we only use 5% of our heart capacity as well. Just think of the great exploration before us as we move into the untapped areas of the heart and the great evolution of our potential for love.

"Thad, how come there are hardly any men in your classes?" I asked.

"A lot of my students complain that they can't meet men that understand this process. In the last course I taught there was only one man, and he was gay!" He laughed and continued: "The men just don't seem to have the same desire to open up. I had many of my students who wanted their partners to learn about the energy work to enhance their sex life and their emotional connection, so I gave a few seminars for couples. It just didn't work! I found myself, first of all, having to pay an inordinate amount of attention to keep an eye out on the men so that they wouldn't hurt themselves doing the yoga, since it was all new to them. And then I had to continually admonish the women not to be so impatient with their partners. The women wanted to experience the energy opening and deeper connection with their boyfriend or husband immediately and were creating an atmosphere of pressure. I never got to teach what I really wanted to impart to get the flow going," Thad explained with a boyish bemusement and disappointment as we both laughed at the apparent futility of the eternal battle of the sexes.

I lay on Thad's table so excited about the exploration I was embarking on, as always. Something always happened on the table that would not disappoint. Now it was time to go inward again and see what was to be shown to me out of the depths of my being.

How can we follow our soul calling, when we don't know our true nature? My sessions with Thad were like a portal back to my true nature. All pretenses or self-consciousness were stripped away. There was no ugly or pretty either physically or emotionally, no need to hide a thing. And through the layers of different specific emotions that would present a new realization as to how I was *wired*, there was always a fundamental, basic element that I could call my true nature--that was this ecstatic bliss--an uncontainable joy that would writhe my body into a vehicle to explore the vast space that is consciousness: a dance of spontaneous, creative postures that expressed the wilderness inside. Again, and again, always something new to behold and wonder at.

It felt as if what lay inside, emotions of joy, energy awakenings and epiphanies of human nature were as endless as the cosmos with its uncharted solar systems and universes. And the boundless, bottomless vastness of the inner psyche was not overwhelming but was safe and comforting. Safe, because it was apparent through my new sensibility that the divine intelligence was so tangibly guiding infinity. Anything that can guide infinity is a power so much greater than I can comprehend, so much greater than anything I know; somehow it makes me feel taken care of in this exploration of the outer limits of my being. Comforting, because it was such a relief to realize that I am so much more interesting than even I knew. I did not have to worry about life getting old or boring when I had access to these inner realms that never ceased to impact my whole being into a new level of feeling alive. Life does not get old on this path. I understood what the living practice was. I was living the mystery, swimming in it. I was it and I was daring to look in the mirror. And it was more comforting to me that it was endless to explore and perhaps even impossible to understand--than if the answers were so simple, finite and fixed. The fact that the mystery is so grand and infinite only means to me that the whole shebang we are in is so great, it can't fit into a human-mind box. And accepting this is a relief!

This type of psyche exploration of wisdom and knowledge is imparted in such a way that to know it, you must become it. Then you are the knowledge that resides in your cells. You are one: mind, body, and soul with the energetic vibration of understanding. It is through such a state of union of fully embracing the truth, that real wisdom is attained.

And yet, out of the safe sanctuary that was Thad, it seemed like to the rest of the world I would have to squelch and hide this most basic ecstatic nature I had discovered. And although the inner critic we all have was much more silent these days, I still had to struggle with the critical voices that make the gazillion excuses as to who and what I had to do and be to deserve to be loved. And how silly and false an impostor this voice is when I have a direct line to this love and acceptance for no reason at all, when I am this ecstatic bliss. The battle between my heart and my programmed mind continued, but for the time being, the heart was winning out.

Lying on Thad's table as his breath synced with mine, as our heart rhythms aligned, I would pass through hazy personality layers that clouded my connection to my true nature. And suddenly, like a rocket blasting through the stratosphere, I was flying in space unhindered by the normal restraints of the boxed-in mentality that defined me as small, beyond all that I was taught were the normal laws of existence.

There seem to be two sets of rules: one that applies to conventional societal norms of life and one that applies to astronauts of altered states exploring infinite consciousness. And upon re-entry to normal life there is always a new negotiation, integration that must take place. And this has proven to be an interesting challenge for me. I want to stay out there in the stars with my heart open to all, but there seems to be a survival instinct or perhaps an old tribal mentality that makes me feel like I need to fit into the societal box again upon re-entry and be accepted within these confining parameters that keep us struggling for love. Not being understood for my soul-traveling ways was a risk for me still. I didn't want to be set apart for having so much true joy. I know it doesn't sound right, but when you're actively expressing bliss, most of the time people seem to think you're crazy. They are far more comfortable and less threatened by an indifferent face.

I keep telling myself to this day: Why do I make so many apologies for who I am, when what I have found at my core is such a positive discovery? Why do I make so many excuses to keep the joy in check? I need to stop apologizing for not being the superficial success story that I'm told will make me accepted and loved, and I need to stop apologizing for the irrational joy that I can experience. How could I forsake this joy for some mediocre mindset and conventional, detached mentality?

I guess it takes a new kind of courage I still have to grow into, to be that joyous self, untethered outside of Thad's safe, allowing sanctuary. To open up to this joy and love there is a vulnerability that instinctively I feel is not always safe to open up with everybody. What could happen? Is my fear founded?

At one point I hope I become tired of worrying about how to negotiate this with others by holding back the joy to suit their level of comfort. I hope to embrace my true joyous nature unabashedly and stop wasting the precious moments of my life. I have to get to the point where I fully allow myself, at all times, the best thing I have known, the inner bliss communion, the hell with everyone else.

As Rumi would say:

"Your task is not to seek love, but merely to seek and find all the barriers within yourself that you have built against it."

This process of awakening is like an entity unto itself, seeking and demolishing all the barriers within me that keep me from love and communion with Spirit.

Thad simply approached the table and my Spirit took over and moved in me as breath of fire: quick, rapid breaths. My body moved on the table as usual. The kundalini sweat dripped down my body. Thad's scent swirled about with the mystical, tribal music opening up my sense memories taking me down the now familiar path to the outer limits of my being.

My body moved fluidly, like a snake, like a wave, until it suddenly hit a sweet spot, a shape that held an energetic truth and locked in a pose that generated a new state of mind. The poses had meaning that linked me to a lesson that I was to grapple with that day.

Through giggles of pleasure and joy suddenly the journey took a serious twist. I found myself in a pose that revealed to me truths of great beings. Bubbling up from inside, this chosen day, was something special which I had never perceived with my old mind set: the understanding of what it was to be so committed to peace, that I could not waste my energy in one moment of violence.

Images of aggression throughout the ages came to me that were so vivid, real, and raw, taking me down, kicking me to the ground, and putting a boot on my head so that I could test and experience this new state of absolute non-violence perspective. Down the emotional rabbit hole, I could feel the echoes of mankind's hate and fear grasp and grip me from blind prejudice, greed for resources and wealth from those that would destroy me if I did not acquiesce to their tyranny, if I did not surrender into a dehumanizing and subservient role that gave them the mad power and security that they sought. Images of great conflicts and humanitarian struggles flooded my mind as I incomprehensively went beyond my individual consciousness and traversed through time, scrolling through histories of shameful crimes against humanity. My hair stood on end and goose bumps announced a heightened state of arousal and true realism of great trials of the human soul and consciousness as the Spirits of great conflict and unimaginable courage entered my body.

I was the black man marching for freedom during the American Civil Rights movement. I was the lowliest of the cast system of India standing up for liberation from British Colonialism. There was no looking in the mirror and seeing a specific face as I relived these episodes, but I was them, looking out into the world from their heart's mind perspective. And in that frame of mind I was empowered to fight, but with not one iota of desire or impulse to commit an act of aggression out of fear for my life. I didn't fear death. The only thing I could not live without was the connection to the sacred which violence would sever. Death could not take away love, the sacred connection, only hate and violence. This experience was a perception tour through what has been described from many as the state of mind of saints.

At that moment, I would have preferred to die rather than raise my hand in any form of aggression, even if it was in self-defense. I understood

Gandhi's state of mind, *Satygraha*, what he must have tapped into to lead a non-violent life for the duration of that specific pose I was in.

Then Spirit contorted me into more yoga positions and this state of mind evaporated like fog, but left my being fragrant and fresh with the dawn of the possibility of a noble and confident state of mind to carry myself through life.

Thad worked deep in the muscles that I seemed to be accentuating with my movement. And when he stepped away to change the music, sometimes my hands would do the work for him. Instinctively, urgently, my hands would knead and prod my own body, crazed to release the energy and keep going deeper. My cellular wisdom had been awakened and my hands had a mind of their own. I was deferring to their instinctual wisdom. The intelligence in my hands was a gift and it sent me into much awestruck gratitude and into deeper release and realization.

Then I was locked in a new pose, on my knees and arms stretching up, wringing and kneading my hands and forearms and at the same time stretching up as if my hands were bound and I was tied to the roof. Then my arms reached into the ethers as they came down outstretched to each side as a gesture of welcoming into me the intelligent power of the universe…and I felt a sense of surrender that was complete.

Up bubbled the understanding of sacrifice for spiritual truth itself. I understood what it was to place the importance of the many above the self. I had a sense that I would bear, endure any ridicule or struggle so as to bare this most beautiful truth of the sacredness of our hearts, our beings, even when faced with death. I felt I was the sacrificial lamb. I was in the state of mind that allowed me to peer through the integrity of such brave spiritual leaders like Martin Luther King, Jesus, or Joan of Arc, who were not able to forsake the truth even when confronted with death.

Now, granted I was safe on a massage table in Venice under the guidance of an energy body worker, but inside of me the inner landscape and stakes that were presented were as real but distant from my true physical reality. I was so deep and lost in an inner world that gave me a life and an understanding far beyond the life I had lived and the points of reference I had known as Suraya.

Where did all these complete altered states of mind and understanding come from? Can you chuck up these new mindsets to chemicals released in the brain? I don't think so, although I do believe certain chemicals are released in these altered moments that accompany a more complete access to our whole being/body/brain. There was an intelligence that guided the whole experience that was not preconceived by my conscious mind.

We do not have to get caught up in semantics (God, higher-self, intelligent design, Life Force Energy, kundalini) or feel that we need to know exactly what or how this intelligence originated. We can just be aware that there is an intelligent force that can open us to new perceptions, mindsets that are valid experiences that evoke a transformative process that can lead to greater compassion and great satisfaction in this human life. I believe these experiences can be of great value to society as a whole. And as time goes on, we can all contribute to the understanding of what this intelligence is-- but we are better off if we don't wait for complete understanding, which may be endless, before we accept the value and reap the benefits of accessing this intelligence.

I feel I was being given a peek into higher altruistic states, spaces from which to conduct and live one's life that come about when the truth of the eternal soul and the core of love and communion with all life are revealed.

I was shown the place from which there is no fear of death. I was being shown not to fear standing in truth even when confronted with death.

One on a spiritual path such as myself could deduce past lives of greatness out of the understanding of such states of mind, but I cannot. No great understanding of past lives was attached to this experience. I was simply being shown the layers and depth of my being. I was being shown the possibilities from which to live by. I was being shown from the collective pool of human experience lessons in truth and divine love.

Finally, my body was spent as such a journey was very emotional and my whole being was recruited into this highly charged energetic experience. I collapsed on the table to rest. Thad went back to his craft, but sensing my exhaustion just caressed me in a comforting and loving way, seeing that I was due a break. But the caresses often work just as well to take me deeper into my experience of self and existence, but that day it just lulled me into a deep sleep, the kind of sleep that when you wake you don't know who you are or where you are for a split second, a refreshed blank-slate consciousness. Then the journey of inner perception flooded back with warmth and new wisdom and body bliss renewed.

24

"Blood Diamonds and Poo Poo Platter with My Consciousness, Please"

Fa, La, La, La...Fa, La, La, La, La. Tis the season to be jolly. Fa, La, La, Fa, La, La, La, La, La.

The Widower and I had continued to see each other steadily over the couple of months leading up to the holidays. There was an even steadiness to our growing feelings. The fluttering in the heart of a new crush was still flitting around us holding us in good keep. Although I had the key to his house and he had told me he was in love with me from the first date, the magic question of 'will you be my girlfriend' and the substantive conversation that leaves no doubt, that must be spoken, not assumed, of 'let's be exclusive" had not occurred, yet. Some would've assumed that the gesture of the key to his house would mean such a thing, but I never assume. It must all be declared or there is no commitment. It is open.

The weekly group channeling sessions continued and the spirits oddly still never advised me. I was sure it was due to the fact that I made it clear vibrationally, with an attitude that I did not attempt to hide, that I had no interest in their form of hokey spirit charades of supposed intergalactic enlightened beings that paraded through to admonish, shame, victimize and filch a person and his friends in the name of spiritual teachings.

Oh! And the tantric report must be given! The tantric exploration wasn't unfolding as I had imagined. The "flow" had not evolved and blossomed, yet. The tantra seemed to stay at the level of "heart orgasms" after the vaginal orgasms and that was new enough to keep me fascinated for the time being.

What was more important for now is that we had a strong chemistry, the addictive kind, the kind that is singular to that one person and is a natural blinder to others, our eyes were just for each other. It is that lust/love combo that locked us into our own world and gave us the confidence to move forward. So even if the "flow" was not there yet, I was open to the fact that it may take more time for us to open up together to those juicier layers of energetic, sexual and spiritual connection that was part of my spiritual quest and path and perhaps, hopefully the greatest love I'd ever know.

On Christmas I walked into The Widower's house and the lights were low. Candles flickered in the corner of my eye and I turned to see an elegantly, festive table set for two. I saw a cozy arrangement for a romantic dinner that was a far better idea than sitting at his large dining room table. The man knew how to create the atmosphere for a special occasion.

The Widower came out from the depths of some back room in his large home with a jolly grin on his face that made it seem like his whole body was smiling; even his pelvic bone, knees, and belly button smiled. The Widower was one Jew that loved to celebrate Christmas and although he didn't put up a tree that year, he had his heart in the day.

"Wow. This is beautiful!" I exclaimed. He didn't say a word and just kissed me with the fullness and feeling of a man in love. He took my hand and led me to the table.

"I had the cook make a very special dinner for us. I'll be serving you tonight," he announced, as he went to collect the dishes of food from the kitchen.

Four months into our relationship things were still new and the desire to get to know one another was still fresh and exciting. We flirted not to seduce each other physically, but to seduce each other into a love and a life partnership, wanting to share the stories that would give us a sense of the life we missed together and the life we may have ahead of us.

The silver trays were emptied as we both tended to eat a lot. The food was so delicious, I was working on scooping up the last traces of gravy on my plate.

"Are you ready for dessert?" my most attentive lover asked.

"Sure. What is it?" I asked, more out of wanting to accept this meal he offered as gift. So I had to be gracious and embrace it, especially on this special day, for I hadn't sought out desserts since starting my raw meat diet.

"Hmm, hmmm…I have a few things that are spectacular, but it is a surprise," he teased in a dastardly villain voice, as he disappeared into the kitchen and almost as if he had gone through a revolving door in which someone did a dessert hand-off, he came back out with a tray of desserts in his hand.

"This is the chocolate, praline torte, this is the classic apple *tarte tatin*, this is the berry ice-cream cake…" as soon as he put that tray of desserts in my face I felt repulsed. It was akin to having someone offer me a plate of poop and as he listed the variety of desserts it was as if he was offering me a platter of varying shit!

"No. Thank You. It looks…" I swallowed with a bitter look on my face as if I was tasting the disgusting shit "…great, but please, no. The strangest thing is happening. I can't eat dessert. I would love some fruit, if you have some."

Before, when I would go to a new gourmet restaurant I would order several of the desserts on the menu to try a cross sample of their pastry delights. Just a few months before this time, I would have tasted all of them with gusto, but now the desire for such sweet things no longer existed in me. I used to love Haagen Dazs ice cream, but now the thought of it repulsed me.

This was not a mental disgust, this was a physical cellular aversion – a very visceral reaction. I was coming to realize that this journey of consciousness was a whole-body remodeling. In certain states of mind that I was experiencing, more and more habits that did not support this new Spirit/emotion/mind blossoming were falling away naturally.

At this time, my craving for raw meat dominated my palate. It was what satisfied me most. I could feel my nervous system relax, my body felt nourished, and I had more energy than ever: a calm, more centered energy than I ever had.

Perhaps habits and desires are inspired by your state of mind. I felt that a new, higher level of intuition was guiding my desires, my likes and dislikes, my habits. There was no struggle for these positive changes. It was happening so naturally. My higher nature had new needs.

The Widower devoured a few of his desserts guilt free and watching him do so did not bother me at all. I ate my fruit and it tasted like the most scrumptious of desserts to me and I enjoyed watching my lover satiate himself, equally.

"Are you ready for your present?" he said mischievously.

"You got me a present? I love presents!"

"But you have to do me a favor and let me prepare you for it."

"I have to prepare? O.K. It sounds mysterious. What do you want me to do?"

"You have to let me undress you to give you your gift."

"Oh, I get it. You are the gift."

"No. It's not me."

The Widower unbuttoned my shirt cuff and kissed the underside of my wrist and lingered to take in my scent. He pulled off my boots and massaged and rubbed my feet. He kissed them as if he were tasting a dessert. He loved my feet! The ritual disrobing was sensually delicious as he peeled and kissed and took in my skin. Once my clothes were all off he did that once-over with his eyes that guys do when they're smitten.

"Now for your present," he said, as he took my hand and led me to the bathroom. I tiptoed behind him trying to keep the sexy aura, but I was cold and shivering. Perhaps he would take my goose bumps for arousal.

"Now, look in the mirror," he said as he stood behind me and gathered my hair and placed it down my back. Then he reached around my chest and placed a diamond necklace made of many hearts linked together around my neck and kissed my neck passionately. It was a stunning way to get such a present. He had a flair for showmanship.

"I hope you're O.K. with the fact that I like to give jewelry."

"It's beautiful! I love it!" I said as he barely gave me time to speak and kissed me passionately. He began to get the heat rising in him and began to make love to me on the bathroom counter in front of the mirror.

"This is definitely better than a partridge in a pear tree, baby. Loved the whole thing, but I need to put something on now, for I'm frickin freezing."

"Well, that is what your other present is for."

He pulled out another box he had hidden and opened it. He pulled out a designer silk evening cloak one might wear to a gala event and wrapped me in it. Ahh!

"Now you are my princess," he said.

We put pillows on the floor in front of the fireplace and lay in each other's arms to enjoy the rest of our evening. The sentiments of love made everything magical and we felt so special together lying in front of the fire, making up for lost time of our lives we had before we met. We kissed and cuddled and talked and felt through all the craziness with which we were challenged, with the hope that the love we were opening to may be for the rest of our lives.

And in the ins and outs of the "getting-to-know-you" conversation I got that strong nagging hit, again, that The Widower wasn't telling me the whole truth about what he really did for a living. And that feeling led to a story that popped into my head out of the blue that flowed out of me as if there was a moral, like in fables, that had to be shared.

"One of my best friend's father is a very successful businessman, but he wanted even more than he had and so he decided to do a business deal with the mob of a very powerful country," I started.

"What kind of business?" he engaged.

"I don't know. I just know that he struggled for years having one business deal after another go to pot and then he finally hit it big. He became very wealthy overnight, but that wasn't enough. Sometimes nothing is ever enough for some people. But the point is he was caught in illegal business deals and is wanted by the FBI. Whatever he did, he can never come back to the United States," I shared, not aware that the Life Force Energy was intuitively baiting him through me to confess that which I felt was hidden and unspoken about his life.

"What kind of guy was he? Is your family still friends with him?" his curiosity followed the story.

"He is a great, loving guy. Their family used to travel often with us. They are still great friends with my family but we only see my girlfriend since her father and mother would be arrested and taken off to prison if they were caught in the U.S. It was super hard watching my girlfriend go through the shock of learning what her parents did, though. She can only go see them abroad since they can't come here anymore. You'd never guess he worked with the mob by just meeting him. Just a regular, warmhearted, cuddly, down-to-earth guy" I said, assuring him of how open my family and I are to the human frailties in life.

"Well, I'm going to share this with you, because you are so intuitive, that you know I'm hiding something from you and if I don't tell you, you'll never trust me and eventually you'll leave me. I know you need to trust me if we are ever going to have a life together and I feel you can handle the truth…" He stopped as if he gave himself one last chance to avoid divulging the secret he kept from me about his life…but he continued…

"I work for the mob," he confessed. I felt my whole body blush in shock. The air became thick, holding me so tightly in the present moment, time stood still. Nothing else existed, but the fire, the living room, me, naked with diamonds, wrapped in silk, and The Widower. Then even all that fell away and none of it existed and I was in a place suspended in feeling the new reality before me. I know I baited him with the story, but it was an unconscious strategy and I didn't think that his confession of that *something* I knew he was hiding would be that he worked for the mob!

"…He sees you when you're sleeping. He knows when you're awake. He knows when you've been bad or good…so be good for goodness sake. Oh! You better watch out…"

More and more dramatic incidences like these were unveiling the wisdom and knowledge of the Life Force Energy hidden in the subconscious. The channel for a dialogue with this higher self was growing. I was being shown that I wasn't very conscious of much at all, but I was awakening to the connection with the Larger Self, the overlord that watches us as if trying to get us to wake from a dreamful coma. The Higher Self that knew The Widower worked for the mob sent me that story from the abyss of my subconscious special delivery to bait him to divulge the truth…

"I'm a financial consigliore for different mob families. I'm a money launderer. I move money around the world with the collaboration of governments and businesses to make their illegal earnings work into the stream of life in an apparently legal way," he confessed. Seeing that I was frozen for words and was looking at him as if he were a stranger, he started to search for something to endear himself to me again.

"Just so you know, whatever money I make I do pay my taxes through my businesses that I launder my money through," he said with a little cuteness and self-effacing humor.

Great! At least he pays his taxes, unlike my other boyfriend, right? Hmmm. One guy makes legit money and doesn't pay his taxes and the other makes his money illegally, but pays his taxes. Ha! What a barrel of monkeys!

...Don our new gay apparel...Fa, La, La...La, La La...La, La, La...Santa Claus had some really new gay apparel this year for me in my diamonds and silk finery!...Troll the ancient Yule-time carol...Fa, La, La, Fa, La, La, La, La, La. I was looking for an angel to unravel the ecstasy of sacred sex and I may have found an actual troll!

One thing I've seen time and again is that what is apparent in my intuitive subconscious mind, a realization--whether good or bad--can be a huge surprise and shock to my conscious mind. I couldn't believe that this man, who I met at meditations and in India at an Ashram and who was developing shows on spiritual healers, worked for the mob!! That was not what I was hinting at when I kept telling him that he was sneaky and that he wasn't telling me the truth about what he did for a living.

"So you've never hurt anyone, have you?" I asked in this jolly Christmas sharing.

"No. If I had pledged to one family I might have had to "make my bones," but I couldn't do that!"

"What the hell is "making your bones?" I said, thinking this was all too unbelievable.

"That is a term that means: make your first kill as an initiation ritual into a family. You have to kill someone to show loyalty and to show that you'll do anything. There is no turning back once someone has something like that on you. No. That wasn't for me. I was an acupuncturist and an artist, for crying out loud. I found a way to work independently for many different families," he said, ready to really spill the details of his can of stinky beans.

"Come on, you're making this up. You just learned that from the Sopranos or something," I insisted, clinging onto the last chance that he may be pulling one of his pranks. He didn't give my question any credence and looked into me, trying to assess the damage.

"How do you feel about all this? Can you handle it?" he asked with a quiver in his voice and holding me even closer, letting me know he was scared of my reaction. I was silent. "I understand if you can't accept it, but it's better if I know now if you are going to leave me than later when we're even closer."

I saw a kind man who seemed to be trying to be a good father. I saw someone who cared to help others heal by introducing them to healers and spirituality through his TV series. I saw a man who was very loving with me, but I'd only known him for a couple of months romantically. He wasn't physically hurting anyone, after all...

"I can't date someone in the mob," I said feeling cold inside no matter how close I was to the roaring fire.

"Just so you know. I'm leaving the "life." I can do that, because I don't just work with one family. Tell me, don't you believe a person can change? I can't do it anymore. I want to go from the darkness back to the light. I just want to help people through my shows on healers and channeling. I'm done with that life of secrecy and nefarious characters. I hope this makes a difference, because I don't want to lose you. I promise I'm leaving the business. Just give me one year to ease myself out of it."

Ahh! What a juicy question. How much can a person change? Do I really believe in redemption? I was waking up to so many new things myself, why couldn't he transform too? He seemed to be sincere. Isn't that the great story you hear in the bible of Jesus forgiving and through his love uplifting those around him out of their depraved minds into a new life of spiritual liberation?

"Yes. I believe people can open their hearts and redeem themselves," I concluded. He held me close and I felt him wipe a tear.

"One year then. And I'm out!" he said.

"The only people I ever told this to was my last wife--because she was very intuitive like you and I had to tell her the truth--and I told my daughter, a few years ago. I took her to dinner and I explained everything."

"How could you tell a fourteen-year-old?"

"I felt that if anything ever happened to me, if I disappeared or died mysteriously, she had to know the truth. Boy, you're right. It was a big mistake, though. I remember when I took her by force to Promises Drug Rehabilitation in Malibu, as I left her there she was screaming at me in front of everyone: Money launderer!! Money launderer!! How can what I do be so bad?!! You're a bad person, not me! I'm going to tell everyone you are a money launderer!" He laughed at his own tragic drama. "Yeah, it was a mistake to tell her alright."

"How did you go from being an acupuncturist and a producer to working for the mob in the first place? Wa, wa, wait, you just said your daughter went to drug rehab?" I said, suddenly flooded by the thick stew of drama I was walking into.

"Ah, those are stories for another time. It's Christmas!" he said in a soothing yet firm tone. I was deep enough in the bowl of relationship soup that I was going to stay and see just what was in this mystery stew of my new tantric lover's life anyway, so I agreed to put such burning, turbulent questions aside. After all, it **was** Christmas!

I realized my new lover, a widower, a mobster, happened to be a Scorpion in the Zodiac. That night he went from being The Widower to The Black Widower, as I realized his shadow side, that we all have, may be venomous…deadly!

"O little town of Bethlehem how still we see thee lie. Above thy deep and dreamless sleep, the silent stars go by…Yet in thy dark streets shineth the everlasting Light. The hopes and fears of all the years are met in thee tonight."

* * *

Thad's Rule of Four Training was turning out to be the most intense study of the human psyche and trauma that I had ever had in my life. The course was teaching us how to unleash the blocks that keep us from experiencing our core, full awareness of who we are on an energetic and intuitive level. So I was now becoming equipped for the beginning of my initiation into experiencing first-hand the convoluted dark side of human beings as that of a mobster trying to rehabilitate and re-humanize himself.

Fa, La, La, La, La…La, La, La, La….

25

"Soul Song"

The New Year was coming and the stage was set for a whole new life, a new way of thinking and a whole new kind of relationship with men. I was ready for a deeper relationship than I had ever had in my life, with a new depth of honesty and a new focus on going deeper into my being through a more energetically aware sexuality that was now accessible and growing in me. It was a profound satisfaction that all the years of spiritual practice and study had brought me to a place beyond my dreams.

I used to read books about the journeys of others waking to the deeper truths of existence and now I was the main character at the center of my own prodigious journey of awakening of the highest order. I experienced a sensation of fullness, an acute and almost painfully sweet fulfillment that was so satisfying as I realized that I was in this new stream of energy, the kundalini, that was a wide and strong current taking me to the pinnacle of my potential destiny. I was in the highest flow of my life streaming toward the highest blooming of my consciousness, my being, uncontrollably headed to crash and settle on the shores of God realization, that made me feel utterly real as no other journey, adventure or quest has.

Every step of the continued awakening was pure satisfaction even if at times it was painful or difficult. This is where I want to be at all times: whole and perfect in my destined and highest flow. It's amazing to surrender to my inner current, the kundalini, with the force and crashing rapids that come as new perceptions and altered states rearrange my inner works and I feel a sense of complete security that all will be well, for this Life Force provides me with the ultimate confidence and trust that I will meet my greatest destiny if I just let go, let go, let go. This intelligence is the intelligence that created everything around me, spiraling and orbiting out through the solar system and through endless space, to the expanding edges of the cosmos.

My father joined us for breakfast and as is his favorite hobby, he was sorting his vitamins at the kitchen table.

"Hi Micha!" he asked as I downed my usual six raw eggs in a cup and prepared my raw coconut cream shake that is part of my raw diet now. The kundalini fanned the flames of my appetite and I was often ravenous upon waking.

"Hi Pa!"

"How's everything going? How's everything with the boyfriends?" he asked, as he always wants the headlines of my life in our quick visits. He was not privy to my tantric sex quest.

"I'm good, I'm really good," I said, accessing the nuances of my thoughts and emotions. "I have a new boyfriend now."

"Really? Has he paid his taxes? No more guys at risk with the law," he said, chuckling at his own humor.

"No, he pays his taxes." I laughed at his joke as well as for the secret declaration I had just received about my new boyfriend's career of laundering money for the mob.

"I feel amazing, so many good things brewing, but a little sadness this morning mixed in. I spoke to Double Double with Cheese and he doesn't sound like he's doing so well. He wants to take me to dinner. I'm feeling that middle place between the old and the new and wishing that one of these days I won't have to say good-bye to one of these guys," I explained, sharing the specific mix of my momentary state that particular morning.

"I say good riddance to him, not good-bye," said my dad. "Who needs someone who is going to be so stupid to get himself in trouble with the IRS because he forgot to pay. And then he can't handle the stress of the mess he got himself in. He was also always overpromising things and under-delivering. Tell him he had his chance and it's too bad," he said with his characteristic snicker that turned into a full-blown laugh as he relished in his caustic joke a bit more.

"He is a good guy. He was a good boyfriend until the IRS issue," I defended him.

"Yeah, he is a good guy," he said and paused. "Just a rat." He laughed again.

Then he looked up from his laughter and sorting of vitamins into cups and really looked at me.

"Wow! You look so good lately!" he said, with an abrupt change of his mocking mood and tone.

"That's funny. I feel a little mashed this morning."

"Your eyes are floating in space and, and the space is in your body," he said with startling passion and poetry and insight unusual for him. I was so taken aback I let out a little giggle.

"Bright, yet diffused. They are protected in light. You can see so much emotion. So many people hide it. They don't let you see it," he continued. "Ethereal. Like you're from another world. They're so beautiful these last few months."

"Must be the new makeup," I said finding a practical answer, as is usually his role to do, helping him to reclaim his cynical nature, lest he forgot himself.

"No. It's the glow," he confirmed.

"Wow! Thanks!" I said almost at a loss for words, shocked for being seen and recognized at a soul level by my skeptical, atheist, irreverent father. But every now and again he lets me see he is way more insightful, sensitive and understanding than he allows any of us to know.

"That's how I can tell the intelligence of my students, the eyes. Some are so bright and others are flat, dead." He paused and looked away lost in thought, wistful. "It's amazing how you can see so much in eyes."

"Yeah, I know what you mean," I said, as I had discovered eyes to be the window to the soul when I started meditating. "Well, Pa, I'm going to get going. Have a good time with your vitamins," I said as I put my hand on his shoulder affectionately.

"Ok. Bye Micha! You're doing good whatever you're doing. It's working for you," he said and we hugged.

I was called by my inner being, the Life Force Energy, to meditate, so I went to my bedroom and sat in front of my altar with all the many pictures of saints and masters from different traditions that I've dabbled in. I closed my eyes and my consciousness immediately sank so deeply in my being that I had the sensation of passing through the walls of my limited awareness, floating into expanded consciousness.

Suddenly, as if in a vacuum, all the air was sucked out of the room. The sound disappeared! The bird chirping and the lite rustle of the wind outside went mute. The faint tinkering of my father in the kitchen was dead silent. The groans and drones of our modern amenities that one takes for granted as constant white noise: air conditioners, the neighbor's pool heater, the generator up the block and cars on the street below my hill all stopped. The silence was so complete and thick it was as if all breathing had stopped as well, and the planet was devoid of air.

In my mind's eye I was in another place, deep in the realms of existence that were revealing themselves to me, a waking dream state where spirit communicates. I was entering a room that I had never seen before. There was a TV screen, showing static only, that I passed by with the understanding that the static was my emotions! An annoying, pointless noise, but then the emotions reflected by the static screen, like the sound in the room, were sucked away too; and in this state, they did not affect me. I was freed from the confusion and distraction of the inner noise they created.

I turned away and saw a bright shining light dancing on a large flat surface. The light started to flicker a bit and slow down. I was able to see that it was actually a reflection off of a spinning silver rectangular plate, like an army dog tag. It originally spun so fast at first it just looked like a dancing spark of light. The reflection was of a brighter light that was the original source of all light.

The light was a humming prayer being chanted over and over as it spun. The prayer it chanted was for the healing of the people of the world. There was so much pure love in the prayer and a soft one-pointed conviction. In that vacuum, silence, and stillness of emotions, I heard my soul, and it was chanting like a Buddhist prayer wheel for healing incessantly! The light and the prayer song are my soul song, my vibrational truth!

For those who've never heard of a Buddhist prayer wheel, I will explain. It is believed that sending prayers out into the ether benefits the world and keeps up a constant wave of beneficent energies that envelops those that lend a hand to spin them as they walk past them in the Himalayas. It is said that waves of compassion and love emanate in all directions from the prayer wheel. So the clever Buddhists came up with a wonderful idea of sending prayers out faster and or continuously to benefit us all through these prayer wheels.

I've never used prayer wheels, but I discovered one inside my heart. I became aware that at the centermost core of my being my soul never stops praying and although most of the time I can't consciously hear it, it is the song that compels me to dance through the world as I do. And I realized that that was the core of who I am: My purest self, unencumbered or affected by my personality or my emotions. And no matter what goes on at the surface, my soul essence is in a perpetual prayer song that compels me to fulfill this wish, the prayer itself. I discovered yet another deeper layer, affirming how truly beautiful beyond measure and yes, sacred, I am, we ALL are!

Our soul is always singing a song, humming a prayer. Everyone has a soul song, a prayer, a mantra that is our true soul desire. Even more than a desire, it is the essential vibration of who we are, our purpose, but you must quiet down the emotional mind static enough to hear it!

We have busy little souls that vibrate like the wings of bees, imperceptibly rolling us toward ecstasy…together.

This was the purest experience of my essence I have ever had. I heard my soul and I perceived it as a prayer wheel for love and healing of the world. How blessed I felt when even for that one moment I heard the song of my soul in its purest form. I was living the magic! And it was more real, dynamically more heartbreakingly beautiful than anything I have perceived in the external world–except, maybe, for the shine in the eyes of others who can also hear their soul song. You can make love to those individuals through the eyes.

To this day, when I start my meditations, after bowing and asking energy assistance from those whom I consider great spiritual teachers in the different dimensions in which they may abide. I then bow in remembrance of the spinning prayer wheel that is my soul song, asking for healing of the pain of the world. I pray that I hear my soul song clearly, steadfast, so that it may guide me more and more to live my heart's purpose in all that I do in life. You don't ever forget experiences such as these, ever! I think that my heart and mind usage/capacity expanded by a few percentage points that day!

It is said in the Tibetan Buddhist tradition that simply touching the prayer wheel brings great purification to negative karma and obstacles. I touched my prayer wheel in the very core of my being and the mere realization that it exists and that it is who I am in the centermost part of my being is liberation, satisfaction itself. It is the love that heals and the truth that burns the karma of illusion. I am not who I thought I was.

I am a vibrational being of love and prayer for the awakening of love as self in all!

My soul song is sweetly, miraculously audible now. The light my prayer wheel can reflect emanates stronger. I am ready for the next crazy, astounding adventure in love, work, and the quest for sacred sex, so that it may continue to show me my greater human potential. I jump in. I freefall into the great mystery of the divine in human form unfolding.

Thad, The Black Widower and the Conscious Life Force Energy (God) dance with me, teaching me to behold it all, gloriously intertwining, braiding life into a strange, rare, and brilliant story, a story that is teaching me a personal relationship with myself and the world in terms of energy. As this knowledge and awareness unfolds, it is a journey into pleasures of my inner being told only in very ancient spiritual scriptures.

I could never have imagined the force of God, the magic of a multi-dimensional reality within the soul, the drama and upheaval of the normal, known and safe life that comes with a true spiritual awakening. Even with the great power of my imagination, I am giddy to say I can't possibly imagine what awaits me. Driven by the power of God itself, unleashed through the kundalini energy expanding and enlightening, I experience the ecstasies and agonies that come out of the great unknown. What is to come on my spiritual path to continue to free my soul, to turn the dial to a permanent blissful state of mind that holds a living relationship to the sacred connection to all aspects of the manifest world? After all the extraordinary events that I have experienced, what could possibly await me in this energy revolution?

While I wait for the next spiritual orgasm to overtake me in a new and unexpected way or the next epiphany to leave me awestruck and humbled in the endless love and grandness of existence, for now I'll take out the trash and start designing my new office furniture. Always another home improvement project lurking, don't you know? I'm just a normal woman living the life of a spiritual ecstatic, a bodhisattva, a Buddha or enlightened one in the becoming...as we all are, on different junctures of the road.

The night after I heard my soul song, I had a dream. I was floating in abstract dreamtime when I was seriously startled by the large face of the lioness roaring inches from my nose. It scared the bejesus out of me. Then I was in my bedroom with the lioness by my side. We started walking simultaneously and the full-length window dissolved . . . and like walking from one set to another in the back lot of a movie set, we walked right out of my bedroom into the Amazon Jungle. And with the first step into the fresh forest night air, an expression of joy sung out from every plant and life form, a symphony of energy enveloped us. I could see, hear, and smell acutely, like never before.

I felt a kinship with the lioness and as we continued to walk, I felt like I was falling in sync with her steps. And as I began feeling my felineness in movement and spirit, I too was growing in a new vitality and power. We picked up the pace. I noticed I was naked, but it was natural, safe, and comforting, as Eve is depicted in the Garden of Eden. We walked on, and out of the corner of my eye I suddenly noticed the lioness had turned black. I looked down startled and her eyes were bright green. She had become a black panther!

I questioned the transformation of my dream companion and wondered if it was a dark omen, but in a flash the question dissipated. I thought to myself, "My soul has taken me this far, so I trust it to take me farther into the abyss of greater awareness of who I am, into the unknown I trust." I smelled freedom, and it felt too good.

Just then I fell to my knees, but I was still gaining pace alongside the panther, and as I looked at my hands, they were black paws. I was becoming a black panther too! With the thrill of freedom, we broke out into running leaps into the jungle, full of adrenaline and exhilaration.

All my life I've longed to be free. What planted that seed in me? The God instinct that planted it in all of us. And as I have grown, I have gained freedom in increments and sometimes in grand leaps towards awareness of what it is to be fully alive. The lioness in me is always breaking free from another cage, wanting to be wild in its true nature, whole and complete.

This is not the end of the tale by far, but just a taste of the beginning of the cosmic, spiritual, sexual exploration that my Higher Self guided me to seek. Now, finally having chosen my first tantric lover, I'm ready to immerse, melt, absorb, explode, unwind, and free my body and soul into the boundless bliss of God and the Evolution of Orgasm.

...Yes, this is merely the beginning of my amazing journey into God and the Evolution of Orgasm!

Coming Next in the Series

"The Channler,
The Healer,
The Necrophiliac Cultist,
And Me!"

…To receive notifications about upcoming books, lectures, and events
go to **www.godandtheevolutionoforgasm**.*com* or
email us at **godorgasms.com**

Glossary

Asanas – Specific positions for the body that cultivate awareness, relaxation, and concentration such as in yoga or meditation.

Bodhisattva – A Sanskrit word that means a "Buddha" (enlightened one) in the becoming.

Coex System – A **COEX System** (Systems of Condensed Experience) is a concept coined by Grof (1976) to describe the way the human brain organizes its experience. A COEX is basically a set of related experiences organized around a powerful emotional center or initially impactful experience. COEX Roots and COEX systems are also shaped by ideas and archetypes.

Conscious Life Force Energy - The all-knowing, pervasive intelligence that is in everything that guides creation. It is beyond the capacity of the intellect and can only be understood through direct experience of the individual. It is the essence of self, higher self, and an intimate understanding of God as energy beyond all human-resembling images or icons as a point of reference for God.

Kundalini – The primordial cosmic God Force energy that resides in the base of the spine dormant until awakened by certain practices. The aim of all yoga and meditation is meant to rouse this force and bring it up the spine purifying the subtle nerve centers (Chakras) and awakening the higher spiritual centers. This energy is said to be the evolutionary force in man capable of fundamentally transforming the psyche and personality to the highest expression of what it is to be a human being. This state of awakening is often called "enlightenment."

Full Body Orgasm – An orgasm that circulates throughout the entire body instead of the localized genital region. It uplifts the consciousness into divine, sacred communion – a spiritual ecstasy.

God Orgasm – A divine communion that floods a being's entire mind, body, heart, an every cell, in ecstatic rapture. It is a state in which a person's consciousness is flooded in total beauty, love messages and guidance from the God-Self. When one's energy channels are open, it can be stimulated during sex, after a vaginal orgasm, through meditation, massage, dance, music, nature, and at times just breathing. The Full, Body Orgasm is under the umbrella of the God Orgasm.

Maha – A Hindi word meaning greatest, powerful, mighty.

Nityanda – (1897-1961) was an Indian guru and Hindu saint. His teachings are published in the "Chidakash Gita." Nityanda's teachings and the power of giving shaktipat--transference of divine energy--were brought to the United States by Swami Muktananda, who founded the Siddha Yoga Foundation, that has ashrams around the world. The current head of this tradition is Swami Gurumayi Chidvilasananda.

Parmahansa Yogananda - An Indian Guru that founded The Self-Realization Fellowship, a worldwide organization to disseminate his teachings. Central to Paramahansa Yogananda's teachings, which embody a complete philosophy and way of life, are scientific techniques of concentration and meditation that lead to the direct personal experience of God.

Rule of Four – Thadeus Young's process of accessing a person's work on his or her blocks to help open to experiencing energy body/the Life Force Energy. The four aspects to access are: 1) emotional trauma and stresses, 2) physical trauma from injuries and surgeries, 3) tightness/lack of flexibility, and 4) toxicity due to diet and environmental causes.

Saddhus (also spelled Sadhu) – Is a religious, ascetic monk, or any holy person in Hinduism and Jainism who has renounced the worldly life. The Saddhu is solely dedicated to achieving moksha (liberation) from the cycle of birth and death, spiritual enlightenment through meditation and contemplation of God. It is thought that the austere practices of the sadhus help to burn off their karma and that of the community at large. Thus, seen as benefiting society, sadhus are supported by donations from many people.

Samadhi – A state of meditative consciousness where the mind becomes still and is merged into oneness, the Supreme Concsiousness of the divine. There are different levels of Samadhi and the answers to this existence and of worlds beyond in other dimensions are attained.

Siddhas – A siddha is one who has attained siddhi, i.e. "power, prowess, strength, ability", a special kind of psychic and supernatural, miraculous, occult power.

Siddhas (Tamil 'Great thinker/wise man', Sanskrit,"perfected one") is a term that is used widely in Indian religions and culture. It means "one who is accomplished". It refers to perfected masters who have achieved a high degree of physical as well as spiritual perfection or enlightenment.

Tantra – Literal translation means loom, weave, system. It implies "interweaving of traditions and teachings as threads into a text, technique or practices.

It has come to mean practices and rituals that bring about union with God within the body and in this physical world. In the West, tantra always connotes a sexual practice that is meant to bring the experience of God realization. There are many other tantric practices that have nothing to do with sex. Tantric practices include mantras (sacred sounds) and yantras (sacred symbols).

Notes

About the Author

Suraya has a diverse background in arts, media, and health. She has grown from being a professional ballet dancer to launching a successful New Age music label to writing scripts for Oscar-winning producers. A speaker and authority of spiritual exploration, she is currently developing a Spiritual Health & Wellness brand. Suraya lives in Los Angeles, California, where she continues to deepen her exploration of human potential in the fields of health and expanded states of consciousness and enjoys her newfound sport of playing Polo.

Contact: godorgasms@gmail.com